THE SEA INSIDE US:
Water in the Life Processes

THE SEA INSIDE US:
Water in the Life Processes

by

STEWART M. BROOKS

MEREDITH PRESS / New York

Copyright © 1968 by Stewart M. Brooks

First edition

Library of Congress Catalog Card Number: 68-15205
MANUFACTURED IN THE UNITED STATES OF AMERICA FOR MEREDITH PRESS
VAN REES PRESS • NEW YORK

ANNE OF P.E.I.

She's mostly water but
she's kind of special

The Author wishes to thank all those who helped during the writing of this book. Especially, he thanks his wife, Natalie, and his son, Marshall, for their comments and criticisms, and Marie Litterer for the excellent illustrations.

Stewart M. Brooks

CONTENTS

INTRODUCTION

Much has been written about the sea around us. Much is still being learned about the oceans and seas as explorers plunge deeper and deeper into these awesome depths. But what about that little known sea inside us? After all, every living thing on earth today, plant and animal alike, can trace its early beginnings back to the sea. Yes, science tells us, all living things had their origin in the sea. And today living things are still waterbound. Take the watermelon or the cucumber, for example. The watermelon is 99 percent water. The cucumber is 99 percent water.

Humans are no exception. Scientists have made the staggering discovery that the human body is mostly water—the adult 60 percent, the baby 80 percent, and the embryo 97 percent! Furthermore, it is now known that very often the difference between health and disease is nothing more than a matter of water—too much water, too little water, or water in the wrong place.

We are now about to take a fascinating excursion into knowledge of the seas of the body—seas not unlike those we swim, sail, or fish on—an excursion which will show why body water can indeed mean the difference between life and death. Too, along the way we shall come across a galaxy of spellbinding events having to do with the processes of life.

To start, however, we must first gain an understanding of certain basic ideas about the human body that have come to light over the years through the combined efforts of men of science and medicine. Every one of these ideas will be explained as it is encountered, so that the reader will understand how the water in his own body functions throughout life.

THE SEA INSIDE US:
Water in the Life Processes

chapter one

BODY FLUIDS

All living things, plant and animal, are composed of a living substance called protoplasm. Further, protoplasm is organized into unbelievably small units called cells. And we can compare a living thing to a brick house, where the bricks represent the cells and the cement between the bricks represents the fluid between the cells. This fluid is called the intercellular fluid.

The amount of intercellular fluid between cells varies considerably as does, indeed, the amount of cement between bricks. For example, the cells of the upper layer of the skin are so tightly packed together that we must use an extremely powerful microscope to see any intercellular fluid at all. But the cells of the blood quite literally float along in the intercellular fluid.

Why is it that living cells are surrounded by this fluid? It is really quite understandable when we consider that each cell must be supplied with the essentials of life (oxygen, sugar, minerals, vitamins, and so on) and the only way these essentials, or nutrients, can pass through the cell membrane and on into the cell itself is in solution; that is, dissolved in water. Just as important, how else could waste products make their exit from the cell unless they too were carried out in a dissolved form?

But in order to see the body as a whole we must extend this picture. That is, where do the nutrients dissolved in the intercellular fluid come from, and where do the waste products dissolved in the intercellular fluid go?

Quite simply, the nutrients originate in the food we eat. Through the process of digestion, carbohydrates, fats, and proteins are broken down in stages by chemical means until all the large molecules are reduced in size to water-soluble molecules; that is, molecules small enough to squeeze into the billions and billions of blood capillaries imbedded in the intestinal wall. And as the blood circulates around the body these tiny nutrient molecules are carried along. Eventually the molecules escape from the blood capillaries among the cells and enter the intercellular fluid. From here, they make their way through the cellular membrane and into the cell.

Waste products—for example, urea and uric acid—travel in just the opposite direction. In other words, they make their way out of the cell and into the intercellular fluid, and then into the blood capillaries. Finally, when the blood passes through the kidneys (the body's waste pumps) the wastes are filtered out, changed into urine, and excreted from the body.

In a broad sense, we might say that the body is an organization of trillions of cells immersed in an intercellular sea, a sea which serves as the means of transporting nutrients and wastes to and fro. Central to this is the fact that this intercellular sea is 99 percent water with a dash of table salt—sodium chloride—and a pinch of five or six other simple chemicals. Moreover, protoplasm, the very stuff of the cell, is mostly water. Thus, in a very real sense, water is life and life is water!

Life originated in the sea and made its way to land only when the forces of evolution put together an organism able to take along a little of the sea with it. Put another way, the intercellular sea—the fluid which bathes the cells—is another form of the primordial seawater. Although modern seawater is much saltier than intercellular fluid—because the rivers are continuously washing mineral salts from the earth into the seas—the proportions of salt and other chemicals are just about the same in seawater as in intercellular fluid. And so, we can regard the human body not only as an organized mass of a trillion-odd cells separated and surrounded by an intercellular fluid, but also as two interrelated biological seas—the intercellular sea (the intercellular fluid) and the cellular sea (the water of protoplasm).

Still, all this might seem a little farfetched when we look around us, for unless it has just rained or someone has just gotten out of the shower, life on land strikes us as often being rather dry and quite parched. But this is an illusion, because a sponge can appear to be quite dry and yet prove to be full of water when it is squeezed. And so it is with plants and animals. All we need in the way of proof is to place a specimen in an oven to drive off the water and then weigh the residue. If a piece of cucumber is used in this experiment, the residue will weigh about 1 percent of the original specimen!

Interestingly, life is pretty much a road of progressive dehydration, for with age comes the loss of water; the

"97 percent embryo" becomes the "80 percent baby" and the "80 percent baby" becomes the "60 percent adult." However, these are only average figures, and between two people there may be a drastic difference in water content. A very thin person, for instance, may have a water content of 70 percent, whereas a fat individual may have a water content of as low as 45 percent. Most people would assume that the opposite should be true until it is recalled that fat and water do not mix!

Returning to the body's two seas—the intercellular and the cellular—let us get practical for a moment and talk about pints and quarts. For example, what is a man's "sea profile" like if he weighs, say, 150 pounds? Assuming the man has an average build, he contains within his body 60 percent of 150 pounds, or ninety pounds of water. In round figures this amounts to about forty-five quarts of water (one quart of water weighs about two pounds). A teen-age girl or boy weighing one hundred pounds contains sixty pounds or thirty quarts of water.

We can break down this sea profile even further. Two thirds of the body's water is cellular and one third of the body's water is intercellular. For example, our 150-pound man with his forty-five quarts of body water has a cellular sea of some thirty quarts and an intercellular sea of some fifteen quarts, and our one-hundred-pound teen-ager has a cellular sea of some twenty quarts and an intercellular sea of some ten quarts.

Blood consists of almost one-half water; to get an idea of how much blood there is in the human body we simply take 8 percent of the body weight. Thus, our one-hundred-pound teen-ager has around eight pounds—or four quarts

—of blood! A quart of blood, like a quart of water, weighs about two pounds.

The fluids of the human body and the seas of the earth contain common table salt, sodium chloride, and an assortment of other chemicals. Unless the amounts of these chemicals remain constant, or in the same proportions at all times, the body is headed for trouble. A simple experiment illustrates this. If a rabbit is killed by a single, painless, powerful blow to the base of the brain, and its heart is removed immediately, the heart will continue to beat normally for hours if it is kept moistened with a solution of essentially the same chemical makeup as the intercellular fluid which bathes the cells. The heart behaves abnormally in all other solutions and refuses to beat at all in plain water! The same is true of all cells, tissues, and organs of the body. In order to sustain life the biological fluids must contain just the right chemicals, and in just the right amounts.

chapter two

OSMOSIS

Tide in. . . . Tide out. . . . Water is always on the move, whether along the seashore or along the cell membrane. But the striking thing about the movement of water within the human body is that the movement is balanced. Water is continuously flowing through the cell membrane in both directions—into and out of the cell—and in such a way that the total amount of cellular fluid within the cells and the total amount of intercellular fluid surrounding the cells are the same at all times.

When blood is examined under a microscope, the red cells look like perfectly shaped pancakes. The cells will remain perfectly shaped as long as they remain in their normal intercellular habitat. If, however, for the sake of experimentation, red cells are separated from blood and added to distilled water (water free of all dissolved materials) a most interesting thing happens to the cells —they swell up and burst! This happens because more water is going into the cells than is going out. If, however, red cells are added to strong salt water, they shrivel and shrink! They shrivel and shrink because more water is going out of the cells than is going in.

This is proof that water not only flows in and out of the cell but, what is more, unless the flow is balanced the consequences may be disastrous. Cells swell and sometimes burst when more water flows in than flows out; cells shrivel and shrink when more water flows out than flows in. Cells will neither swell nor shrivel as long as the water exchange is balanced!

The explanation for this intriguing swelling and shriveling of the cell is found in one of nature's processes called osmosis. Osmosis is the movement of water through a semipermeable membrane separating two solutions. A semipermeable membrane allows water molecules to pass through it freely, but not the molecules of other substances. In the living cell, the cell membrane is semipermeable and therefore osmosis is always going on between the cellular fluid and the intercellular fluid.

There is a definite law for the process of osmosis. The main flow of water is from the solution with the least dissolved particles into the solution with the most dissolved particles. That is, the main flow of water is from the less dense solution to the more dense solution, the "denseness" being determined by the number of dissolved particles in solution. The reason for this is simple. The less dense solution has proportionately more water than the more dense solution, with the result that water will flow into the denser solution to equalize the amount of water on either side of the semipermeable membrane.

Thus, cells in distilled water gain more water than they lose and swell and burst because distilled water is much less dense than cellular fluid. Cells shrivel and shrink in concentrated solutions because cellular fluid is less dense than the solution, and more water flows out of the cell than flows in.

Although the experiment using red blood cells and the microscope is a good laboratory exercise, we can do almost as well in the kitchen using cellophane, sugar, and water. First, a piece of cellophane is fashioned into a bag and then about half filled with a solution of sugar in water. Next, the neck of the bag is tightly secured with a string and the bag immersed in plain water. In a few minutes the bag will start to swell because more water will be flowing in than flowing out. Let us now reverse the trick by putting plain water in the bag and immersing the bag into sugar and water. This time the bag will shrivel up because more water will flow out than flow in. Finally, if the setup is arranged so that the sugar solution is inside and outside the bag, no change will be noted in the size or shape of the bag. In this case, the solutions are of the same osmotic density, meaning that the flow in and the flow out are balanced.

Normally, the cells of the body neither swell nor shrink; the reason for this is that the cellular fluid and the intercellular fluid have the same osmotic density. Thanks to osmosis, there is a balanced flow of water between the cellular sea and the intercellular sea, which means that the amount of water in the body and in the cells and around the cells is the same at all times.

Tide in. . . . Tide out. . . . Water is always on the move, but in a balanced way!

chapter three

INTAKE AND OUTPUT

We have just seen that water flows in and out of the cells in a balanced way. Now we are going to see that water "flows" in and out of the *body* in a balanced way; that is, the body's water intake equals its water output and vice versa. In a sense, there are two biological tides—the flow back and forth of water between the cellular sea and the intercellular sea and the flow back and forth of water between the body and its environment. And these tides are quite literally connected with each other because in order to have harmony or balance within the body the water flowing in and out of the body must be balanced. If more water is taken in than is put out the body becomes waterlogged; if more water is put out than is taken in the body becomes dehydrated. Either situation, carried to the extreme, can be the cause of death!

On a typical day the healthy body gains about two and a half quarts of water and loses about two and a half quarts. Surprisingly, the gain in water comes from two sources in addition to the fluids we drink, like water, tea, coffee, milk, and so on. One of these sources is preformed water and the other is oxidative water. By preformed water we mean the water content of solid food, which can be astonishingly high. For example, cucumbers, watermelons and lettuce are almost all water. The significance of this source of water is illustrated by the camel. During the winter the camel meets its need for water by grazing on bushes and succulent plants which flourish after rain and contain considerable water. One student of camel physiology found that Sahara-browsing camels commonly refuse water even after long months without drinking.

Oxidative water is best understood by holding an inverted glass over a candle flame and noting the moisture which collects on the inside. In the same fashion the burning, or oxidation, of foods within the cells of the body also yields water. This is just simple chemistry which entails nothing more than the combining of hydrogen in the food with the oxygen we breathe. Burning one pound of fat, the food with the greatest proportion of hydrogen, yields one pint of water!

Oxidative water may play a life-and-death role for some creatures. The desert rat, for instance, may never take a drink throughout its life and depends mainly on this source of water.

Thus, the body's water intake "flows" along three channels—fluids, preformed water, and oxidative water. Fluids average about one and a half quarts per day, preformed water about one and a half pints, and oxidative water about one and a half cups. Thus, better than one third of our water intake comes from sources most of us never think about. But there is someone who does think about them, and thinks about them constantly, and that is the person with kidney failure!

To balance the two to three quarts intake the body must rid itself of two to three quarts. The avenues of exit include the obvious one—the kidneys—and the not so obvious ones—the skin and lungs. On a typical day the body loses about a quart and a half of water as urine, about a pint from the skin as water vapor, close to a pint from the lungs as water vapor, and about a half a cup in the feces. Again, most of us go through life unaware of the fact that over a twenty-four hour period we lose about a quart of water as invisible vapor. But proof of the vapor is close at hand—just blow against a cold windowpane or get perspired doing exercise and you will discover it for yourself.

Perspiration is a ready reminder that the amount of water lost in hot weather increases tremendously. On the desert a man loses up to as much as twenty quarts a day! Less dramatic but not necessarily less serious is the high water loss during a fever, especially in infants. The loss of water from the skin and lungs becomes a serious matter in patients who are being kept alive by intravenous fluids. That is, the doctor must guard against giving too much fluid and must also guard against giving too little. Although a patient with kidney failure, for example, may be putting out very little or no urine at all, he is nonetheless losing at least a quart of water as unseen water vapor. This must be repaid to maintain the intake–output balance.

The balance in the body between the cellular and intercellular seas is regulated pretty much by osmosis. The regulating factors for the intake–output exchange center on the kidneys and the somewhat mysterious sensation called thirst. The thirst sensation is truly a mystery because to this day scientists are not absolutely certain of what exactly it is. Like pain, we experience thirst but cannot describe it.

The most widely held explanation of the cause of thirst is that an abnormal loss of water from the blood—as a result of urination and heavy sweating—brings about, in turn, a loss of water from the cells. Further, a loss of water by certain cells in the brain causes them to send out nerve impulses, or signals. We experience these signals as thirst. Interesting support for this theory comes from certain cases of brain damage and brain tumors where there may be a great desire to drink on the one hand or no desire to drink at all on the other. This is true whether or not the body needs water. A person suffering from such brain damage must be watched closely lest he drink himself to death or die of dehydration, depending on which way the thirst mechanism is affected.

The kidneys are best described as chemical brains, for these two organs select which chemicals should stay in the blood and which chemicals should leave. Just how the kidneys do this has been the subject of much research. Many important facts about the kidneys have been discovered. But despite all this research there remains a great deal more to learn.

Each kidney contains a million or so filtering plants called nephrons. A nephron is made up of a ball of blood capillaries and a fairly long microscopic tube, or tubule, which is shaped like a funnel at one end. The ball of capillaries fits into the funnel portion of the tubule and other capillaries are imbedded in the walls of the tubule all along its length. As the blood flows into the ball of capillaries quite a bit of pressure is built up, enough to force out—or filter—much of the watery portion of the blood right through the capillary walls and into the funnel.

In this watery mixture, or filtrate, are contained countless blood chemicals—some good (such as nutrients) and some bad (the wastes). Logic tells us that most of the water and all the "good chemicals" should be returned to the blood, whereas the "bad chemicals" should be screened out and discarded. This is just what happens. As the filtrate flows along in the tubule, water and the other things the blood needs are reabsorbed into the blood via the capillaries imbedded in the tubule walls. Thus, by the time the filtrate reaches the end of the tubule the only thing that remains is a tiny drop of water highly charged with dissolved wastes. This we call urine.

Although a tiny drop does not sound like much—and it is not—we must remember that there is a total of two million nephrons working around the clock. Together they produce about a quart and a half of urine per day. What is more, in order to produce this amount of urine the nephrons have to filter (and reabsorb) about two hundred quarts of fluid! This involves a tremendous amount of work and energy.

The big mystery, of course, is how the cells which make up the walls of the nephron tubule know what to reabsorb into the blood and what to leave in the filtrate. An enormous amount of research has gone into the study of kidney function, and a great deal is known about it, but there still is not a definite solution to this mystery of the nephron tubules.

Although the kidneys tend to operate pretty much on

their own, outside influences do exist. Two special influences are blood pressure and a certain hormone. The role of blood pressure is understandable because, as in any filtering device, an increase in pressure speeds up the rate of filtration. This can be readily shown by squeezing a cellophane bag filled with water. With a drastic drop in blood pressure, such as is found in cases of shock, no urine is produced at all! For normal functioning, therefore, the blood flowing through the kidneys' two million microscopic nephrons must be of proper pressure.

The certain hormone mentioned is called vasopressin. It is manufactured by the pea-sized pituitary gland located at the base of the brain. Vasopressin, or ADH as it is sometimes called, stimulates the kidneys to retain water when the body's fluids are low; the kidneys thereby conserve water at that time. If, however, the body's fluids are above normal, the pituitary gland does not release the hormone.

It is believed that vasopressin acts by causing the nephron tubule to step up its reabsorption of water. Thus, more water returns to the blood and less is lost in the urine. Apparently the signals to the pituitary gland causing it to release vasopressin arise from the very same brain cells that produce the sensation of thirst. Thus, the signal to start drinking and the release of the hormone cooperate to keep up the body's water level.

Thus, in health the body's fluids are kept in balance because water intake and output are equal. The chief controlling factors of this balance are thirst and the kidneys. When the body needs water we become thirsty and the kidneys cut down their output of urine; when the body has all the water it needs, we are not thirsty and the kidneys increase their output of urine. Finally, the signals which set these controls into operation are transmitted by certain cells in the brain—cells which always seem to know when there is too little water or too much water in the body.

chapter four

ACIDS AND ALKALIES

Chemically pure water, that is, water which is free of dissolved substances, is neutral. It is neither acidic nor alkaline. Most other liquids, however, are at least a little acidic or a little alkaline.

Acidity and alkalinity are indicated by a measurement called a pH scale. Its values run from 0 to 14, with 7 representing neutrality. Numbers less than 7 indicate increasing acidity. Numbers greater than 7 indicate increasing alkalinity. For example, a solution with a pH of 5 is slightly more acidic than a solution with a pH of 6, and a solution with a pH of 9 is slightly more alkaline than a solution with a pH of 8.

These facts of chemistry can help us to learn even more about the biological seas. Our starting point is this: The pH of the intercellular fluid, including the blood, is, in a healthy body, 7.4—a meaningless piece of information until one realizes that a drop below 6 or a rise above 8 can mean death!

Why the pH of the intercellular liquid bathing the cells has to be 7.4 is not really known. But it is known that the chemistry of the cells, particularly those of the brain, goes astray when the value strays away from this most critical point. Below 7.4, a condition called acidosis, and above 7.4, alkalosis, the body is in trouble.

The remarkable thing is not so much that relatively small variation in a decimal point can spell danger, but rather that the body is able to maintain a pH of 7.4 even though an avalanche of alkaline and acid materials is constantly seeping into the blood from within (cellular waste products) and from without (a sour pickle, for instance!). One single drop of acid added to a gallon of water can lower the pH of the water a measurable amount. If blood behaved chemically as water does, the human body would be in constant trouble.

There are three lines of defense in maintaining pH—blood buffers, the lungs, and the kidneys. Buffers are chemicals which have the ability to neutralize both excess acid and excess alkali, and up to a point they enable the blood to take care of itself. This can be easily shown by merely pouring a little blood into a test tube and noting with special indicator paper that it holds its own pretty well even though assaulted by a small amount of either acid or alkali.

But buffers are not strong enough to act alone; blood needs assistance to counteract the effects of large amounts of acids and alkalies. This is where the lungs and kidneys help. When for some reason or other the blood pH starts to drop, certain cells in the brain register this change and send out messages to increase breathing. As a result, increased quantities of carbonic acid, a gaseous acid waste product, escape from the blood into the lungs and are blown off in the breath. Getting rid of this acid reduces the total acid content of the blood and helps to stabilize the body's falling pH. Thus, persons with severe acidosis automatically breathe deeply and rapidly to stay alive!

If, however, the pH of the blood starts to rise, breathing becomes slow and shallow in order to conserve carbonic acid and thereby counteract the rising pH. The body eliminates carbonic acid when there is too much acid, and conserves it when there is not enough acid.

The reader can do an experiment on himself to demonstrate the effect of breathing on pH. For instance, blowing up several balloons without stopping will make you dizzy; holding your breath for as long as possible can make you dizzy, too. Notice also that after blowing up all the balloons breathing becomes, for a few seconds, slow and shallow—just the opposite of what happens after you cannot hold your breath any longer.

The explanation for this is as follows. Blowing up the balloons forces abnormal amounts of carbonic acid out of the blood. This causes the pH to rise (causing dizziness), which, in turn, causes the brain to remedy the situation by slowing up breathing. In contrast, holding the breath causes the carbonic acid to build up in the blood, and the pH starts to drop (this causes dizziness, too) which, in turn, causes the brain to stimulate breathing and thereby eliminate the excess carbonic acid.

The kidneys assist the body in keeping the pH where it belongs by performing certain chemical feats, such as retaining or eliminating sodium bicarbonate (baking soda). Like carbonic acid, sodium bicarbonate is always present in the blood, but unlike carbonic acid this chemical is alkaline. When the kidneys start removing sodium bicarbonate from the blood the pH tends to drop, and when they allow the chemical to build up in the blood the pH tends to rise. Thus, should the pH of the blood for some reason start to drop—perhaps as the result of eating too many sour pickles—the kidneys assist by refusing to excrete sodium bicarbonate. If, however, the pH starts to rise—perhaps as a result of taking too much baking soda for an upset stomach—the kidneys respond by excreting sodium bicarbonate.

Thus, in order to remain in health the pH of the intercellular sea must remain at 7.4, and in order to keep it at this point the body employs buffers, the lungs, and the kidneys.

chapter five

PERSPIRATION

The air is parched and the sand afire. From overhead the
white heat of a ruthless sun streams downward. The temperature is 130°F. The place is the Sahara Desert.

Man alone and on foot in such a place may pull through
if there is an oasis not too far away and if he has sufficient water with him. Without water he will find himself
staggering around in about four hours, and in about eight
hours he will be dead. In a way it is a wonder that he can
last this long because with each passing hour his body
loses at least a quart of water in the form of sweat. The
point of no return is somewhere in the vicinity of eight
quarts.

The idea of a man dying of thirst or, as the doctors
put it, dehydration, is not a pleasant one. Before the end
comes the hapless victim experiences a series of unpleas-
ant symptoms. In the early stages he becomes intensely
thirsty and his physical condition worsens; then his senses
become distorted and his judgment falters. Shortly there-
after he becomes delirious and deaf to all sound. Finally—
and fortunately—he becomes insensitive to pain.

The body has a terrible problem. To counteract the heat

and stay alive, it is sweating, because sweating cools the skin through evaporation. But this is the same thing that causes death through the loss of water. The loss of water brings about death in the following way. As more and more water is lost in sweating the blood becomes thicker and thicker. It flows along at such a slow pace that it no longer carries the rising body heat outward to the skin to be given off to the air. Also, because it circulates so slowly, it does not bring necessary amounts of nutrients and oxygen to the heart, brain, and other vital organs and tissues. Functional failures, like breathing, result.

All this raises an intriguing question. How does the camel manage to beat the heat? Recent studies have disclosed that the camel is just about as amazing as legend says it is. Whereas a man is at death's door with a water loss of about 10 percent of his body weight, a camel may lose 25 percent or more of its body weight without damage. For an average size camel this comes close to twenty-five gallons of water!

How does this ship of the desert do it? The answer is that its blood continues flowing long after the same point at which man's blood has turned to something like molasses. Man should be able to do the same thing. Theoretically, as water is lost from the blood the blood becomes more and more dense. Then, by the process of osmosis, water should be drawn into the capillaries from the intercellular fluid, for the first order of business is to make sure the blood can flow in order to carry away the excess body heat. Interestingly, one scientist who has devoted several years to the study of camel physiology says that the real question is not so much *how* the dehydrated camel maintains its blood volume to beat the heat, but rather *why* a dehydrated man cannot.

In addition to being able to withstand a degree of dehydration that would kill a man, the camel also excels in conserving water. The camel's ability to go without water intake for long periods of time is proverbial. Until the present time one explanation for this has been that it has some sort of built-in reservoir in its hump, in one of its many stomachs, or elsewhere in the body. It certainly appears to have a reservoir, for its enormous drinking ability is true enough. One thirsty camel is reported to have lapped up thirty gallons of water in a mere ten minutes. But so far all kinds of dissections of camels have failed to turn up any such reservoir, and as for the hump it does not contain water at all! It contains fat! In other words, the camel, like man, drinks only enough to satisfy its present needs and stores no water at all.

The camel's ability to excel man in going for long periods of time without drinking water can be partially explained on a basis of water conservation. In the heat of the desert the camel loses water much less quickly than does man. There are four interesting reasons for this. First, the camel's body thermostat allows its temperature to climb up slowly to 105°F., whereas in man the body thermostat is set at 98.6°F. and stays right there. In order for man's temperature to remain at 98.6°F. a quart or more of perspiration an hour has to be lost in the cooling process! In contrast, the camel does not start to perspire freely until its body temperature reaches 105 degrees. Too, during the cool desert night the camel lowers the heat load on its body still further by letting its body temperature drop drastically. At dawn it may be down to 93°F.! In man the temperature remains 98.6°F. day and night. Thus, as the scorching sun rises from the dunes man starts to pour out perspiration on the spot, whereas the camel has a safety margin of twelve degrees (105 — 93) before its perspiration starts to flow.

Another reason why the camel is able to conserve water can be found in its natural insulation of hair. Even during the summer, when the camel sheds much of its wool coat, it retains a layer several inches thick on its back, on which the sun beats down. The value of this hairy insulation was proved a few years ago when scientists discovered that shearing the wool from a camel increased its water loss by almost two-thirds! The wearing of a thick wool coat on the desert sounds farfetched, but the Arabs, like the camel, know better. We are all familiar with the picture of the desert dweller attired in several layers of loose heavy clothing.

The third reason for the camel's ability to conserve water is the hump, which helps out in an unexpected way. Unlike practically all other mammals which have their fat distributed almost uniformly over the body just beneath the skin, the bulk of the camel's fat is located in his hump. Since fat slows the flow of heat outward, the camel loses proportionately more heat from its other body surfaces than does man and as a result has less need to perspire.

The fourth and final reason is that the camel, like the desert rat, has a pair of kidneys which produce a much more concentrated urine than man's, so that proportionately much less water is lost in this way. Man's kidneys do not have this power of concentrating waste.

Even with these aids for the conservation of body water, the camel does lose large quantities of fluid during long, dry trips. But there is still no explanation as to why the camel can safely lose such a high percentage of water and why man cannot.

Luckily, few of us are forced to compete with the camel in desert heat. Nevertheless we do get into conflict with the thermometer from time to time. For example, during the summer months and in places where people are compelled to work in extreme heat (furnace rooms, launderies, steel plants, and so on) "heat exhaustion" is common.

Surprisingly, a form of heat exhaustion called "heat cramps" often occurs even though the water loss is paid back immediately by drinking water or other fluids. Perspiration contains a fair amount of salt which must also be paid back if the body is to function normally. Heat cramps, therefore, result chiefly from a lack of salt rather than a lack of water.

Heat cramps affect only a few bundles of muscle at a time, never an entire mass of muscle. As some bundles relax, a neighboring group contracts, and vice versa. In this way, the cramp wanders painfully through the muscle. If a man gets an attack while lifting a heavy weight, cramps may hit the arms, legs, or belly, sometimes quite severely.

Excessive sweating, then, calls for water—and plenty of salt—to counteract it.

chapter six

EXCESS SALT

Without drinking water the castaway on the sea is no better off than the man staggering on the dunes of the Sahara. "Water, water everywhere, nor any drop to drink. . . ."

But why ". . . nor any drop to drink?" Why is it that man cannot drink seawater? So what if seawater is salty? In order to understand the answers to these questions let us find out just exactly what happens when excess salt is taken into the human body.

Salt is absorbed into the blood capillaries of the intestine and eventually seeps into the intercellular fluid surrounding the cells. As a result the intercellular fluid becomes more dense than the cellular fluid and, by the force of osmosis, draws out abnormal amounts of water from the cells. This excess water in the intercellular fluid now spills over into the blood, and from the blood spills over into the urine.

In other words, salt draws vital water right out of the cells and sends it into the urine. An efficient job is done, too, because for every quart of salt water the castaway drinks his kidneys are forced to get rid of one and a half

quarts of urine. The result is dehydration—and a gallop-
ing dehydration if the castaway is exposed to sun and
wind. Under such conditions he will lose two quarts per
day in perspiration alone.

Nor can a man lost at sea improve his position by drinking urine because this is as salty as the water about him.
Urine and seawater, however, can be put to use to cool
his clothing, and thus himself, by evaporation, thereby
cutting down on his water loss through perspiration. Eating raw fish does not help because all the water available
in the fish is needed to dissolve and excrete the waste
products resulting from digesting and burning fish protein.
Although a man might gain some water by drinking the
juice extracted from fish muscle, no one has yet been able
to devise an effective method of doing this in a small boat
at sea because the juices of the muscle are held so tightly.
Man cannot safely venture out on the sea without an
assured supply of water or one of the devices which re-
moves the salts from seawater.

If man cannot drink seawater, what about seabirds?
Like the camel and desert rat they are especially equipped
to handle the problem of water supply, but it was not
until 1956 that their mechanism was understood. In that
year Knut Schmidt-Nielsen and his colleagues discovered
that the double-crested cormorant eliminated excess salt
through two so-called nasal glands situated in its head.
Interestingly, these glands had been incorrectly understood to protect the lining of the nose by producing a
secretion which rinsed away seawater when it got into the
nasal cavities.

The nasal glands extract salt from the blood and secrete

it from the body as a clear watery liquid. So efficient are the glands that in the cormorant, at least, they can rid the body of all its salt in roughly ten hours. In most seabirds the salty secretions run from the nasal openings and down the beak to accumulate at the tip from which the drops are shaken off by sudden jerks of the head. The birds equipped with this fantastic device include the true marine birds—the shearwater, the petrel, the albatross—and such coastal birds as guillemots, auks, gulls, and cormorants.

Of these birds the most efficient at disposing of salt is the albatross. Its nasal glands are so successful in extracting salt from the blood that the albatross requires huge doses of salt in order to stay alive! This was discovered by Doctors Mable and Hubert Frings in 1957. Until then, the albatross had never been kept alive in captivity for more than a few months. The birds died mysteriously from no obvious cause. Day by day, they grew drowsier and drowsier and weaker and weaker. Just before the end the great birds became unconscious. Cause of death —salt deficiency!

Marine reptiles—sea turtles, sea iguanas, sea snakes, and sea crocodiles—also have nasal glands for extracting salt. They also eliminate a certain amount of salt through their tears. Lewis Carroll undoubtedly knew nothing about the salt but was well aware of reptile tears when he wrote in *Alice In Wonderland* ". . . . So they went up to the Mock Turtle, who looked at them with large eyes full of tears."

chapter seven

GASTRIC AND INTESTINAL LOSSES

In the body of a man of average build the total amount of digestive juices, which are about 99 percent water, produced over a twenty-four hour period by the salivary glands, stomach, pancreas, and small intestine, is about nine quarts—or almost one quarter of his total body water! All but a few ounces of this huge volume of water is returned to the blood in the process of absorption which goes on constantly in both the small and large intestine. Thus, if for some reason absorption fails, water is lost and the body is placed off keel—sometimes in a most serious way. This is just what happens in cases of severe diarrhea or vomiting.

Diarrhea is the medical term applied to frequent and watery stools. Ordinarily the soupy contents of the intestine are propelled forward slowly enough by the wormlike movement, or peristalsis, of the intestine to allow ample time for the absorption of water. In diarrhea, peristalsis is so speeded up and intense that absorption occurs only partially or not at all. Incidentally, the discomfort and pain which usually accompany diarrhea are excellent proof that peristalsis has become overstimulated and excessive.

There are many reasons why peristalsis becomes overstimulated and excessive. The most common cause is infection. Some virus or bacterium present in contaminated food or drink attacks the intestinal lining and sets up an inflammation. This causes irritation and stimulation of the muscles in the intestinal wall. The result is excessive intestinal movement.

Although most bouts of diarrhea are minor upsets, severe or prolonged diarrhea, especially in infants, can be fatal. In severe cases, not only is there a great loss of water, but also of salt, potassium, and sodium bicarbonate. These losses must be repaid in full. Just as in cases of dehydration from sweating, it is important to repay body chemicals as well as water. Failure to repay salt and potassium results in abnormal functioning of the muscles, heart, and nervous system; failure to repay sodium bicarbonate may bring about acidosis and unconsciousness. Sodium bicarbonate is an alkaline chemical. It is one of the body's chief buffers in keeping the pH at its proper level of 7.4. Losing large amounts, therefore, lets the acid proportionately increase; the pH then drops below the desirable level of 7.4.

Moderate losses can, for the most part, be repaid by simply drinking fluids. Severe losses, however, demand intravenous feedings. In these cases, doctors must be very careful to determine the exact nature of the losses. When repaying losses by vein, it is extremely important for the doctor to give just the right amount of fluid—not too much and not too little. The usual way to determine the extent of the water loss is to consider the loss in weight. For instance, if a child with diarrhea loses four pounds, the fluid loss is about two quarts. Since the normal concentrations of salt, potassium, and sodium bicarbonate per quart of intestinal fluid are known, these losses, too, can be quite accurately determined, and the intravenous feeding solution can be made up in the same concentrations.

Vomiting also deprives the body of water and chemical agents. When it is severe, it may prove to be a threat to life, particularly in infants. In most cases the loss chiefly involves the gastric juice of the stomach. Gastric juice has a high concentration of hydrochloric acid; when abnormal amounts are lost, the proportion of sodium bicarbonate in the blood goes up and thus the pH of the blood goes up. The result is alkalosis. In alkalosis, all the muscles usually are contracted and if those responsible for breathing are involved, death may result. Sometimes there is great excitement of the nervous system, causing convulsions very much like those experienced in epilepsy.

To repay the losses of water, salt, and hydrochloric acid, the doctor estimates, as in diarrhea, the loss in weight and divides by two. For example, a weight loss of two pounds is equal to about one quart of gastric juice. Because it would be dangerous to introduce hydrochloric acid directly into the bloodstream, a special chemical called ammonium chloride is used. The body eventually converts this chemical into hydrochloric acid. The amount needed is determined by the volume of gastric juice lost.

Diarrhea and vomiting, then, can dry up the body's seas just as effectively as exposure on a waterless desert. Vomiting deprives the body of hydrochloric acid, and diarrhea washes away vital potassium and the alkaline

buffer, sodium bicarbonate. These are particularly dangerous in infants; death from diarrhea and vomiting used
to be fairly common in the very young before modern
medical discoveries and practices.

chapter eight

BURNS

Burns are among the most hideous, most horrifying, and most agonizing form of injury man can experience. Even with modern medical knowledge, burns are very often fatal when over half the body's surface is involved. The immediate threat to life is shock, a mysterious state of collapse marked by an ashen pallor, clammy skin, cold arms and legs, and, eventually, unconsciousness. Unless shock is treated immediately, the victim may die within a few hours from what might otherwise have been a non-fatal burn.

Shock is seen not only in burns, but also in a wide variety of other disorders, such as severe infections, broken bones, massive crushing injuries, and hemorrhage, to name only a few. This is another medical mystery. Why does the same result—shock—follow such apparently unrelated causes? Scientists have studied this for years, but so far no one has come up with an explanation that satisfies everybody. There is some evidence that shock, in most instances, involves little more than the body's salt and water being in the wrong place at the wrong time.

The sequence in burn shock is believed to be somewhat

as follows. In the area of the burn the blood capillaries become abnormally leaky, so that fluid—chiefly salt and water—escapes from the blood. This causes considerable swelling, or edema, in the affected area. Now because of this loss of water the blood becomes more osmotically dense and starts to draw in intercellular fluid from the body at large—fluid which in turn rapidly escapes from the leaky capillaries in the burned area.

At the same time that this is happening, potassium escapes from the damaged cells and pushes up the concentration of that element in the intercellular fluid. Excess potassium in intercellular fluid interferes with the pumping action of the heart, and can even stop it, so that in a sense, the body is poisoning itself. But this poisoning results not from an excess of potassium in the body. Rather, it results from potassium being in the wrong place. As a matter of fact, the total amount of potassium in the body may very well be below normal levels!

Thus, burn shock results mainly from the sudden shift of salt and water from uninjured areas to injured areas and, to a lesser extent, from the increase in potassium in the intercellular fluid bathing the cells. In other words, because of the injured area, the body as a whole is deprived of salt and water. In theory, at least, the ideal remedy would be to replace the salt and water lost from the uninjured cells, and at the same time to supply all the fluid the burned area can use.

Support for this idea comes from studies involving humans as well as animals. The studies of humans were started fifteen years ago at three hospitals in Lima, Peru, where plasma and whole blood—the accepted remedies of shock—were in short supply, with not even enough on hand to treat emergency patients. Victims of serious burns were given large quantities of saline solution, 0.9 percent salt in water, principally by mouth. The results were excellent. At first there were many predictions of failure. The patients would not drink quarts of salt water, many doctors said, and even if they did it would sicken or kill them. But the doctors found these patients willing to swallow quarts of the fluid, for the dehydration caused by burns brings on severe thirst. Patients unable to swallow were given the saline solution intravenously.

Experience with a now substantial number of patients shows that large quantities of saline solution are in most cases as effective as plasma in the treatment of shock arising from severe burns. At the very least it can be recommended as effective therapy for shock when plasma and whole blood are not readily available.

The treatment of burn shock in the modern well-equipped hospital entails the use of a number of intravenous fluids in addition to saline solution. These include sugar solutions, whole blood, plasma, and plasma substitutes. As in cases of fluid loss from dehydration, vomiting, or diarrhea, it is important to judge as accurately as possible the ingredients and how much is needed so that the correct solution and amount are given.

The best guide to the amount of fluid needed to treat shock effectively and still not overload the circulation is the degree, or severity, of the burn and the area of the burn. The degree of the burn can be determined by the appearance of the skin. In a first-degree burn the skin is reddened; in a second-degree burn the skin is blistered;

Rule of nines

The percentages in this figure refer to body area. For example, a burn involving the entire back and one entire leg would represent a 36 percent burn.

and in a third-degree burn the skin is cooked or charred.

The physician uses the "Rule of Nines" in figuring the area of the burn. The head counts 9 percent of the total body area, each arm 9 percent, each leg 18 percent, the front of the trunk 18 percent, and the back of the trunk 18 percent. Using the Rule of Nines, then, a victim with a burn involving an entire arm and an entire leg has a total burned area of 27 percent.

Once the degree of the burn and the area of the burn have been thus determined, the doctor consults a table which tells him the type and amount of fluid to use. Additional factors also play a key role in treatment. Drugs are needed for pain; antibiotics are needed to fight infection; and skin must be grafted to the most critical areas. At the outset, however, shock and salt and water have top priority. The seas inside us must be in harmony; the seas inside us must be in balance.

chapter nine

BLOOD PROTEIN

Blood, the body's "Red Sea," is made up roughly of half red and white cells and half fluid. Unlike the intercellular fluid elsewhere in the body the fluid, or plasma, of the blood contains a high quantity of protein. The amount of protein in the intercellular fluid outside the blood is just about nil.

There is an excellent reason why Nature put protein in plasma, a reason which has to do with balance. Plasma is constantly subjected to the pressure placed on it by the heart; were it not for some means of opposing this pressure excessive amounts of water would be forced out of the capillaries and into the tissues. The opposing means is protein. Water forced out of the capillaries by the blood pressure is balanced by the water drawn into the capillaries from the surrounding intercellular sea by the osmotic force of the protein molecules. In short, protein "draws water."

Normally, the flow of water between the blood and the intercellular fluid at large is in perfect balance, just as it is between the intercellular fluid and the cellular fluid. This explains why the amount of blood—about six quarts in a man of average size—remains remarkably constant. If the concentration of plasma protein drops, the plasma loses its osmotic ability to draw water into the capillaries; eventually water is lost from the blood to the surrounding tissues. The result is edema, or the abnormal accumulation of water in the tissues—water which rightly belongs to the blood.

Edema, as we have already seen, also occurs in burns, but the mechanics are not the same. Fluid pours into the burned area because the capillaries are damaged. In protein-poor edema, the cause is related basically to the process of osmosis.

There are several conditions and situations which lead to a decrease in the quantity of plasma protein and eventually to edema. In starvation, for example, the body attempts to stay alive by burning up everything which will burn, including protein. This is like burning up the furniture if there is no other fuel available. The edema of starvation, or "hunger edema," was a dramatic medical discovery in the prisons and concentration camps of World War II. A usual symptom is swollen legs, sometimes so swollen and waterlogged that deep pits are produced when the fingers are pressed into the flesh. In severe cases the pits remain for several minutes.

The most common cause of protein-poor edema, however, is in certain kidney diseases where, for one or more reasons that are not completely understood, large amounts of protein escape into the urine. This form of edema is generally very severe and often affects the whole body. The face is especially puffy and the eyelids are sometimes

BLOOD PROTEIN / **39**

so engorged with water that the victim does not resemble his normal self.

The remedy for protein-poor edema seems to be obvious—make the blood protein-rich. Although big juicy steaks (smothered in mushrooms!) represent the most popular treatment, often times in severe cases the patient must be given digested protein in intravenous fluids. In advanced starvation, for instance, food by mouth cannot be tolerated. But whichever way, the prime concern is to get protein into the blood and boost the osmotic pressure high enough to get all that water back into the circulation where it belongs. If a juicy steak will do it, so much the better!

chapter ten

HEART FAILURE

The pressure of the blood forces water out of the capillaries; blood protein, via osmosis, pulls it back in. Normally, then, there is balance. Three things can happen, however, to upset this balance, two of which we came across in earlier chapters—damaged capillaries, as in burns, and decreased blood protein, as in starvation and kidney disease. Both result in an outpouring of water into the tissues causing edema.

The third thing that can cause edema is abnormal blood pressure. When blood pressure becomes excessively high, more water is forced out of the circulation than can be drawn back by the protein. This is what happens in cardiac edema—the edema of heart disease.

The heart is a double pump. The right side of the heart pumps blood to the lungs where it picks up oxygen and releases carbon dioxide; the left side of the heart pumps out the blood after it has been oxygenated to circulate through the rest of the body. After circulating, the blood returns to the right side of the heart and is again pumped to the lungs—and so on and on.

Let us suppose that for some reason, such as hardening of the arteries, faulty valves, or rheumatic fever, the right side of the heart becomes weakened and fails to perform its pumping duties properly. The blood returning to the heart would not be pumped fast enough and would start to dam up, causing the pressure within the veins throughout the body to increase. In severe cases of heart disease this can be seen in the veins of the neck, which look as though they might burst any minute. The increased pressure forces abnormal quantities of water out of the capillaries and into the intercellular fluid of the tissues.

Further, the left side of the heart does not receive enough blood to pump to the kidneys, which means that water is held back in the body instead of being excreted—water which will eventually join the already excess water in the tissues. Again, because the kidneys are not eliminating enough salt, this, too, accumulates in the tissues. Thus, the victim of heart failure stores more and more water and more and more salt until there is swelling from head to toe.

This is bad enough, but left-side failure is even worse. After being oxygenated in the lungs, the blood returns to the left side of the heart to be pumped out to the body at large. If the left side fails, the blood, as with right-side failure, is not pumped out fast enough. However, in this case the blood dams up in the lungs and the excessive pressure forces water out into the air spaces. The doctor's stethoscope can detect this condition, for when the patient breathes there is a "death rattle" caused by the air bubbling through the water.

But there is a life-saving drug called digitalis. When this drug is given in the proper dosage, it strengthens the heart muscle and restores the pumping action to normal. The dammed-up blood commences to move and the swollen tissues gradually begin to lose water, because of the improved circulation through the kidneys. But in severe cases where the body is starting to drown in its own fluid, additional drugs called diuretics are used. Diuretics force the kidneys to produce more than the normal amount of urine, and thus to drain away even more water. Some diuretics are so potent that just one shot will bring about

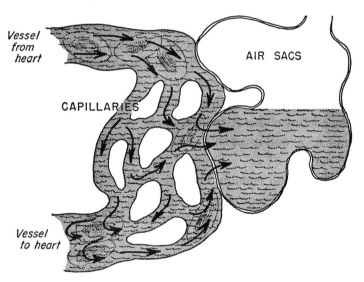

When the heart fails to pump blood out fast enough to keep pace with the return of blood from the lungs, the blood backs up in the lungs. This causes an increase in pressure which forces plasma water out through the capillaries and into the air spaces in the lungs.

the excretion of two or three gallons of urine in a few hours.

In cases of permanent heart damage, the patient must take digitalis for the remainder of his life to keep the heart pumping as it should. But this is a very small price to pay, indeed, when we recall those death rattles.

chapter eleven

ELEPHANTIASIS

When early explorers to the South Sea Islands saw the crystal clear lagoons, stately palm trees, and dazzling, beautiful girls, they believed that here at last was Paradise on Earth. But Nature does not provide a perfect Paradise. Here, on these enchanted isles, was discovered one of the most hideous and horrifying of all diseases—a disease which causes the arms and legs to become so swollen they resemble the limbs of elephants and thus is called elephantiasis, or elephant's disease.

If, for instance, elephantiasis involves only one leg, the leg usually swells to a size two or three times the diameter of the unaffected leg. In some cases one leg may weigh as much as the entire remainder of the body.

This unsightly disease is found throughout the hot, damp tropics, in China, India, Africa, and the West Indies. In some places as many as three out of ten persons may be afflicted. Fifty years ago the disease was not uncommon in the United States; it was rampant in and about Charleston, South Carolina!

Workers have been investigating elephantiasis for the past century, and recent researchers have found that this once mysterious disease is but another form, albeit a most weird form, of edema. This form of edema involves not the pressure of the blood, not the capillary walls, and not plasma protein, but the lymph vessels. The lymph vessels are minute, even microscopic, channels present throughout the tissues which drain away excess intercellular fluid and return it in a very roundabout way to the blood. They are called lymph vessels because when the intercellular fluid is inside them it is known as lymph, although lymph and intercellular fluid are almost the same chemically.

If these vessels are blocked off, the excess fluid which seeps out into the tissues from the blood capillaries accumulates and produces edema. This is exactly what happens in elephantiasis, where worms—thousands of them—make their home in the lymph vessels.

These worms, which are called *Wuchereria bancrofti,* were first studied by Otto Wucherer, a German doctor, and Joseph Bancroft, an English doctor. They look somewhat like pieces of thread and the females are much longer than the males—the female being about three inches and the male an inch or so. They are most primitive creatures with little sense of direction or power of movement.

When these worms mate, the female becomes, quite literally, a reproductive factory, turning out tiny young larvae by the thousands. These young larvae are carried away by the moving lymph and eventually end up in the bloodstream. Here they can be removed from the infected person by a certain kind of mosquito that takes the larvae in along with the person's blood. The mosquito becomes infected, and it is in the mosquito—not in man—that the larvae undergo changes preparing them for adulthood.

When an infected mosquito bites another person, the mature larvae are injected into the human tissues. Here they become true adults, move into the lymph vessels, and mate. Thus, the cycle continues and the infected human in partnership with the mosquito spreads the disease to others.

The role of the mosquito in elephantiasis is of historical interest. In the 1880's a young medical missionary in China, Patrick Manson, discovered and showed for the first time that an insect could be the necessary agent in transmitting a disease from one man to another. Years later Manson suggested that malaria also must be transmitted by the mosquito—a theory which Ronald Ross proved to be true. However, Ross was given the Nobel Prize in medicine in 1902 for the discovery, and Manson was all but forgotten.

Manson also discovered that the larvae of *Wuchereria bancrofti* leave the blood during the daytime and return at night! The scientific world considered this finding a joke and even inquired whether or not the larvae carried watches; but Manson proved the larvae, indeed, may carry a biological timepiece, for they start leaving the blood at one o'clock in the morning and begin returning at four in the afternoon! The mechanism of this timepiece is still not understood. When the larvae leave the blood, they are destined for the lungs, but the question as to why they make this trip is also unanswered.

For the practical problem of controlling elephantiasis, the outlook is good. DDT has proved somewhat disappointing, for the kind of mosquito that carries the larvae is becoming resistant to it, but a drug by the name of

Hetrazan has produced amazing results. When taken by mouth Hetrazan kills off the larvae within an hour, and further treatment kills off the adult worms or injures them so that they are unable to mate. Results with the drug in West Africa, Tahiti, India, and various other parts of the world show that constant use of the drug for the next several years may eradicate the disease altogether.

But killing the larvae and worms does not cure the disease itself, for scar tissue will still block the lymph vessels after the worms have departed. Thus the best hope is for the complete eradication of these "sea serpents."

chapter twelve

GLAUCOMA

There is intense headache and great pain surrounding the
eyes. Everything looks foggy and lights are ringed with
haloes. The family doctor is called. He notes one of the
eyes has a dull gray gleam and is red and inflamed; compared to the unaffected eye, it is as "hard as a marble."
Immediately he calls an ophthalmologist, an eye specialist,
because if his suspicion is correct the patient has glaucoma
and in a day or two the eye could be blinded. Furthermore, the other eye may also be afflicted, for it too has the
seeds of the very same disease.

Glaucoma is at the present time thought to be the leading cause of blindness in the United States. Although this
tragic eye disease principally affects the aged, occasionally it appears in infants as the result of a birth defect.
Thousands of our adult population unknowingly harbor
a tendency toward glaucoma. Progress in the diagnosis
and treatment of the disease achieved during the last
twenty years gives hope that the next twenty years or
so will see a marked drop in blindness. Above all, doctors
and the public should be alerted to the signs of glaucoma

described above. If they occur, one should take immediate action.

Glaucoma occurs when fluid is secreted into the eye faster than it can drain out. (Normally the fluid inflates the eyeball to give it shape and stability.) As a result, the pressure within increases and the eyeball becomes as hard as a marble. If this elevated pressure is not relieved, it will destroy the optic nerve and the light-sensitive part of the eye, the retina. Glaucoma, then, is also a disease of fluid, or water, balance.

The fluid fills the front, or smaller, cavity of the eyeball and is called aqueous humor. The aqueous humor resembles the intercellular fluid and is produced by capillaries located just behind the iris—the colored part of the eye— at a rate of about three drops an hour. From these capillaries it flows through the pupil, or the opening in the iris, into the front cavity. Since this cavity holds only a little over two drops, excess fluid will accumulate in a matter of minutes if anything happens to the drainage system.

The drainage system comprises thousands of microscopic canals—located within the angle between the cornea and the iris—which lead into a larger main vessel called the canal of Schlemm. The canal of Schlemm connects with blood vessels in the outer coat of the eyeball, and thus, the aqueous humor eventually returns from whence it came.

The iris plays a critical part in all this. The iris is made up of colored muscle and has the shape of a flattened-out doughnut, the hole of the doughnut being the pupil. The iris controls the amount of light entering the eye by causing the pupil to get larger in darkness and smaller in

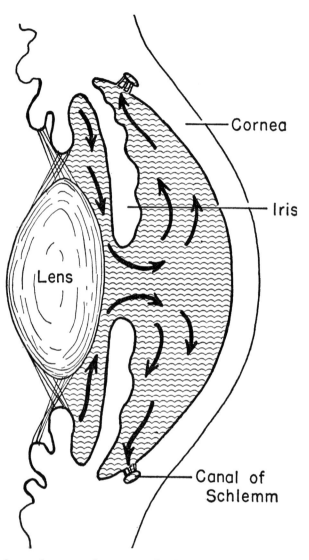

Cornea

Iris

Lens

Canal of
Schlemm

This figure shows a side view of the front portion of the eye. The fluid, or aqueous humor, which fills this front portion is produced behind the iris and flows out through the pupil (the hole in the iris) and then into the tiny channels leading to the canal of Schlemm.

50

bright light. The pupil becomes smaller when the iris muscle relaxes and larger when the iris muscle contracts. In contracting, however, the iris bunches up on itself and thickens considerably in the area of the drainage system.

Ordinarily the thickening of the iris causes no trouble, but if the cornea—the clear outer portion of the eyeball—is too close to the iris, the thickened iris may prevent the aqueous humor from entering the tiny canals. Since the pupil opens to its fullest in prolonged darkness, persons with this type of glaucoma often suffer their first attack at the theater. Excitement, because it causes the pupil to dilate, may also set off an attack.

Thus, in this type of glaucoma the initial cause is the abnormally short distance between the cornea and the iris and the resulting narrow, or closed, angle formed in the drainage area. In another type of glaucoma, called open-angle glaucoma, the angle is normal—that is, "open"—but the tiny canals for some reason become narrowed or clogged. With both types drainage is hampered and thus the pressure goes up.

Fortunately, ophthalmologists today can do a variety of things to relieve, and perhaps even cure, glaucoma—if it is detected early enough. The key word here is *early!* Glaucoma can be detected simply and painlessly with an instrument called the tonometer. All the patient has to do is lie flat on the examination table and keep his eyes open. The doctor places a drop or two of a local anesthetic in the eyes, and then places the tonometer directly over the cornea. In a matter of seconds, the gadget registers the pressure of the aqueous humor in the front cavity. All

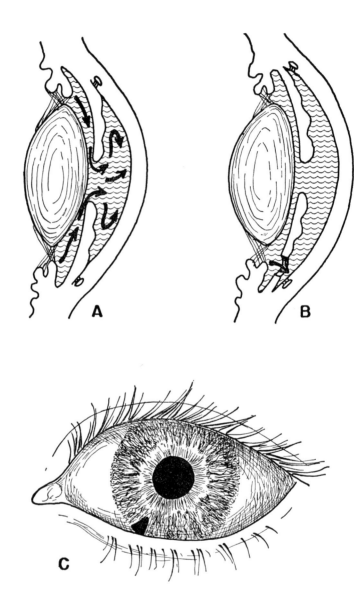

A

B

C

persons over the age of forty should have this test done at yearly intervals.

Once glaucoma has been detected the doctor usually prescribes a drug which constricts the pupil and thus keeps the outer portion of the iris in a thinned out condition and away from the tiny canals of the drainage system. Although this is not a cure, it does reduce the pressure. Eserine is one drug used for this purpose and is placed directly in the eye in the form of drops. More recently a new drug, Diamox, has been used to reduce the pressure by slowing down the output of aqueous humor. Diamox is used primarily in severe cases where the pressure is high enough to cause blindness at any moment. When the drug is given by vein the results are often spectacular. But once again, this is not a cure.

Within the past fifteen years or so it has become possible to cure many cases of closed-angle glaucoma and thus free the patient from a life of continuous use of drugs. The operation consists of cutting out a tiny hole in the

---

In glaucoma, illustrated on facing page, something happens to interfere with the drainage of aqueous humor. The form of glaucoma shown here is closed-angle glaucoma, where the iris and cornea are so close together that the aqueous humor cannot drain into the canal of Schlemm (A). By a simple operation in which a hole is cut in the outer portion of the iris, the disease can usually be improved and sometimes cured. The hole permits the aqueous humor to flow more easily forward (B), thereby reducing the pressure which tends to push the iris forward and "close" the angle. In the normal eye the pushing out of the iris causes no trouble because the angle between the iris and cornea is wide enough to allow for this. The dark triangle in the iris (C) shows what the hole looks like.

outer edge of the iris. Ordinarily, the pressure of the aqueous humor behind the iris is slightly higher than it is in front of the iris, since it is behind the iris that the aqueous humor is produced. This pressure tends to bulge the iris in the direction of the cornea and thereby slightly decrease the all-important angle. Although this effect does not bother the normal eye, in glaucoma it worsens the condition by interfering with the flow of aqueous humor into the little canals.

After the hole is cut in the iris, the aqueous humor can flow directly into the front cavity without taking the longer route through the pupil. Consequently, there is less tendency for the aqueous humor to stay in the space behind the iris and to push the iris forward—decreasing the angle. The operation is quite simple and results in practically no disfigurement of the eye. It is usually successful when performed in the *early* stage of the disease.

Glaucoma involves only a tiny amount of water—literally, a few drops. Such a tiny sea, the aqueous humor—but it means the difference between sight and blindness.

chapter thirteen

HYDROCEPHALUS

Deep within the human brain there are four intercon-
nected spaces called ventricles. The ventricles are filled
with a watery fluid—cerebrospinal fluid—which measures
somewhere around five or six ounces. Cerebrospinal fluid
continually oozes into the ventricles from certain blood
capillaries located in the two largest ventricles and is continually drained away and absorbed back into the blood
by a special system of ducts and capillaries.

This continual flow of cerebrospinal fluid is Nature's
way of keeping the brain and spinal cord moist and pro-
tecting them from various and sudden pressures from
within and without. Under abnormal conditions, such as
a tumor or malformation in the openings or ducts between
the ventricles, the cerebrospinal fluid will begin to accumulate. Often the cause of the accumulation cannot be
detected, but regardless of the cause, the fluid is unable to
return to the blood and thus forces the swelling of the
ventricles and eventually the entire brain! If this occurs
in an infant before the bones of the cranium have fused

Normal ventricles of the brain

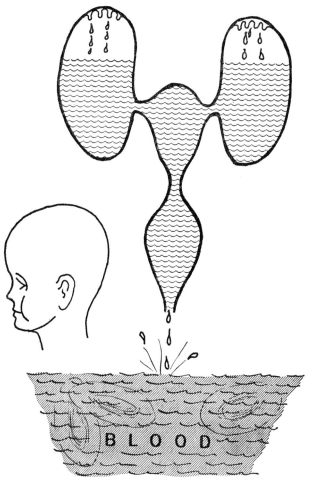

This figure shows the spaces, or ventricles, within the brain in cross section. The cerebrospinal fluid which fills the ventricles is produced by blood capillaries in the roof of the two largest ventricles and eventually drains back into the blood.

together, the expanding brain will push aside these bones and enlarge the whole head—a condition the medical dictionary calls hydrocephalus (*hydro-:* water; *-cephalus:* head).

It is a frightful thing to see. In the severe case the size of a baby's head will dwarf the rest of his body. The scalp is thin and shiny, the veins stand out like overflowing canals of purplish ink, and the "soft spot" is greatly enlarged and looks as if it is about to give way to the tremendous pressure from within.

For a while the brain is able to withstand the pressure, but gradually its tissues are destroyed. In the older child and adult the disease is accompanied by intense headache, strange movements of the eyeballs, slow beating of the heart, slow breathing, drowsiness, mental weakness, and finally loss of consciousness. In the baby, the eyes are apt to be displaced downward and may seem to wander. Most peculiarly the baby may suddenly squirm with much excitement when aroused and handled, an excitement which, in a matter of seconds, gives way to a deep drowsiness and finally unconsciousness.

Until recent years the outlook for victims of hydrocephalus, particularly infants, was most discouraging. In severe cases the situation was the proverbial, "It's just a matter of time." Although some victims were kept alive, few were able to develop normally. Today, the situation is somewhat improved by surgical techniques specifically designed to remedy the cerebrospinal plumbing.

One of the most promising operations presently being performed entails the running of a permanent piece of

Hydrocephalus

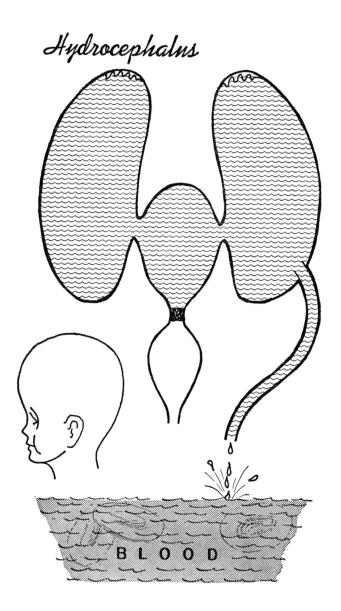

BLOOD

plastic tubing between one of the two largest ventricles and the right side of the heart; this tube allows the cerebrospinal fluid to drain directly into the blood, and is equipped with a valve that regulates its flow.

In hydrocephalus, illustrated on facing page, there is an obstruction to the flow of cerebrospinal fluid, represented here as a "plug" between the middle and bottom ventricles. This causes the ventricles to swell up and expand the head. In one type of operation for the condition, a piece of plastic tubing is run from one of the large ventricles to the heart.

chapter fourteen

DIABETES MELLITUS

Within the pancreas, a gland shaped somewhat like a fish, are clusters of cells called the islands of Langerhans—named after the man who discoved them. The islands of Langerhans produce a hormone—or chemical messenger —called insulin. All the effects of insulin are not yet known and most of those which are known cannot be fully explained. But one thing is quite definite: There is a relationship between the insulin and sugar within the body which is so critical that if it is upset or altered a vicious disease results—diabetes!

This disease afflicts some three million people in the United States alone. In addition, there are a million or so more individuals who have a mild form of the disease and do not know it.

There are two different kinds of diabetes, and since they are not related in cause or treatment, it is most important to distinguish between them. The lesser known of the two, diabetes insipidus, will be discussed in the next chapter. The diabetes of insulin fame is called diabetes mellitus. This term is derived from the Greek, *diabetes,* "to pass through," and the Latin *mellitus,* "honey"—and so we have "honey passing through." This is not only colorful, but also correct, for the victim of diabetes mellitus has sugar in his urine; sugar actually passes right through the body.

This loss of sugar, however, is not all that diabetes mellitus entails, for the presence of sugar in the urine is only a *sign* of diabetes, a sign that all is not well. The body is in the process of starving to death, wasting away, and becoming dehydrated. Too, the diabetes victim is prone

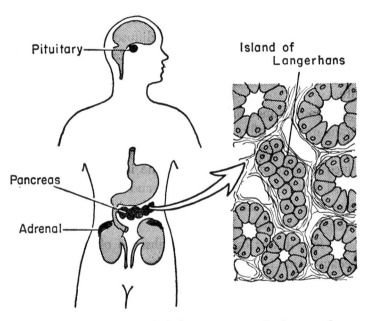

Shown are three glands which have a profound effect on the sea inside us. The blown-up microscopic view of the pancreas shows one of the millions of islands of Langerhans. The "islands" produce and release the hormone insulin to the blood. The chief hormone of the pituitary which affects body water is vasopressin, or ADH. The adrenal glands produce a number of hormones which affect body water and salt.

to infection and his eyesight may fail, leading eventually to total blindness. The usual cause of death is a lowered pH or acidosis! How can all this be explained? Where do insulin and sugar fit into the picture?

All carbohydrates—starches and sugars—are broken down in the process of digestion into much smaller molecules comprised of simple sugars, of which glucose is the most important and the only one involved in diabetes mellitus. Glucose readily enters the blood capillaries of the intestine and in a minute or two is carried by the blood to all areas of the body, where it diffuses through the cell membranes into the cells proper. Once in the cells, glucose supplies the chemical energy essential to the activities of life.

Glucose cannot diffuse or pass through the cell membrane unless insulin is present. In effect insulin opens certain molecular-size doors in the membrane and lets in glucose, although how this is done is not clearly understood. But if insulin is not present and thus glucose cannot enter the cell, the cell will be deprived of life-giving energy. The result: diabetes!

At first it was believed the absence of insulin occurs because the islands of Langerhans are not producing enough. This undoubtedly does happen in some cases, but in the last few years doctors have discovered, paradoxically, that a great many diabetics have ample insulin— some with even an excess!

Yet these very same patients, with a normal-functioning pancreas, are benefited by injecting insulin into their body! One current theory, which receives laboratory support, is that these particular diabetics possess some chemical factor which inhibits their own insulin. However, this theory is not universally accepted and there is laboratory support for other theories, too.

But, although the mechanism is not completely understood, the signs and symptoms of diabetes confirm the fact that glucose is unable to diffuse into the cells. Glucose builds up in the blood and, consequently, the kidneys attempt to remove it, which explains the presence of sugar in the urine. In order to excrete glucose the kidneys require extra water (to dissolve it in), which explains the excessive amount of urine. This leads to dehydration and extreme thirst.

Thus, the victim of diabetes is thirsty, hungry, tired, and weak. Too, he loses flesh because his cells start to burn other substances in an attempt to keep alive. In a word, the body is plunged into chemical chaos and before long all the tissues, organs, and systems go awry. In particular, the retina of the eye degenerates, causing poor eyesight and eventually blindness. Commonly, the slightest scratch results in a serious infection.

The cause of death in most instances, though, is a sudden and sharp drop in pH—acidosis. Unable to get their energy from glucose the cells start to burn more than the usual amount of fat, an event resulting in excessive quantities of fatty acids. A small amount of such wastes the body can take care of with its alkaline defenses—buffers and so on—but in advanced diabetes the pH cannot be held at the normal value of 7.4. The upshot is acidosis and coma.

When a patient is in a diabetic coma, the pH has to be brought up to where it belongs in a matter of minutes.

Too, because of the loss of water and salt, and potassium, via sweat, urine, and vomiting (acidosis often causes severe vomiting) and because of a diminished fluid intake, dehydration must be speedily corrected. Alkaline solutions are started immediately. Further, glucose solutions must be given to supply energy and enough insulin must be given to allow the glucose to pass into the cells.

There is no cure for diabetes, but with proper treatment most persons with the disease can hope to live out their years. The prognosis, or outcome, depends heavily upon the severity of the disease and how early it is detected. (Note that word *early!*) In mild cases a special diet may be all that is necessary. Such a diet is, of course, low in sugars, sweets, and starches.

In most cases, diabetes is treated with insulin, which the drug manufacturer extracts from the pancreas glands of cattle and hogs. Since insulin is destroyed by digestive juices, it must be injected beneath the skin. Some diabetics, however, may avoid the prick of the needle, for they can take certain oral drugs, such as Orinase, which stimulate the islands of Langerhans to produce insulin. Evidently, those patients who are not benefited by these drugs either have islands unable to produce insulin, even when stimulated, or else they have a type of diabetes unrelated to the pancreas. Interestingly, it was these drug failures which caused scientists and doctors to question the early theories about diabetes.

chapter fifteen

DIABETES INSIPIDUS

In diabetes mellitus the urine contains sugar (glucose) and is therefore "sweet," as is indicated by the "mellitus" or "honey" part of the name. An entirely different disease is also called "diabetes," or, more correctly, diabetes insipidus. In diabetes insipidus the urine contains no sugar and is therefore "tasteless." And the term insipidus comes from the Latin *insipidus* which means "tasteless."

Actually, these names are quite unfortunate inasmuch as the "diabetes" part indicates a close relationship between the two diseases. This is by no means true, for other than an excessive output of urine they are totally unrelated. Diabetes mellitus is concerned with the pancreas, whereas diabetes insipidus involves the pituitary gland which is located at the base of the brain. Even though only about the size of a small marble, the pituitary gland is the body's "master gland." It produces over two dozen potent hormones which in some way control and regulate almost everything that goes on in the body. Most of these hormones work indirectly—by stimulating other glands to produce their hormones—but a few work directly on specific tissues and organs.

Actually we have already encountered the hormone involved in diabetes insipidus. It is called vasopressin or ADH—the ADH standing for antidiuretic hormone. In the kidney, it will be recalled, the nephrons, or the microscopic filtering plants, first form a watery filtrate from the blood and from this filtrate reabsorb or take back into the blood all the vital chemical substances, leaving behind unwanted waste products and excess water. The purpose of ADH is to stimulate the nephrons to reabsorb water; the more of the hormone the pituitary gland releases, the greater is the amount of water reabsorbed back into the blood and the lower the output of urine.

The amount of ADH the pituitary gland produces and releases depends on the water content of the blood. When the water content of the blood is low and the body needs to conserve water, certain cells in the brain which are sensitive to this lack of water send nerve impulses to the pituitary gland causing it to step up the output of ADH. In turn, the hormone causes the kidneys to conserve water. On the other hand, when the water content of the blood is up these brain cells send fewer nerve impulses to the pituitary. Less ADH is released and more water lost to the urine. Thus, the pituitary gland through the agency of the hormone ADH plays a major role in maintaining water balance—conserving water in times of need and getting rid of water in times of an over abundance.

In diabetes insipidus there is a deficiency of ADH because a defect in the pituitary gland interferes with the production of the hormone. This could be a hereditary defect or an acquired defect. If hereditary, a part of the gland's chemical machinery is apparently missing or altered, though the gland usually looks normal enough. In other words, the victim is born with a defective gland. By contrast, a victim may have a normal gland at birth, but as a result of a tumor, an injury, or an infection the gland is damaged enough to interfere with the output of ADH. Whether the damage is hereditary or acquired, there is a deficiency of the hormone and diabetes insipidus results.

The outstanding feature of the disease—the output of huge volumes of urine—is easily understood. There is not enough ADH available to cause the kidneys to conserve water, regardless of how badly the body needs water. In severe cases, the patient may excrete as much as twenty quarts of urine in one day! Hand in hand with this, there is an extreme thirst and the consumption of tremendous amounts of water—up to as much as twenty quarts! The patient grows weaker and weaker and in time becomes nothing more than "skin and bones." Without treatment the outcome is fatal.

With proper treatment, however, the patient can be restored to complete health. Indeed, there is perhaps no other disease involving hormones which responds so dramatically to treatment. An injection of three or four drops of the hormone solution given two or three times a week will restore the necessary water balance in the body. However, the injections do not cure the defective pituitary gland and thus they must be continued for life.

The diagnosis of diabetes insipidus provides an interesting sidelight. Though the diagnosis can often be made on the basis of the patient's medical history, sometimes tests are required to confirm the diagnosis. One test—according to some doctors the best—is to have the patient drink several glasses of water and then inhale the smoke of a cigarette. The nicotine in the smoke will enter the blood. If a person has a normal pituitary, the nicotine will stimulate the gland, as the blood passes through it, to produce ADH. Thus the output of urine will decrease even though excess water has been taken. Nicotine does not have this effect if a person has diabetes insipidus because the pituitary gland is not able to produce ADH.

A tiny insignificant gland, quarts and quarts of urine, quarts and quarts of water—these are the ingredients of yet another strange tale relating to the sea inside us.

chapter sixteen

ADDISON'S DISEASE

About one person in 100,000 has a tan that is not an ordi-
nary tan like the one you get at the seashore. It is a tan
that comes from within and is associated with death and
disease—a disease relating to the sea inside us!

Atop each kidney sits a small, triangular, flattened struc-
ture called the adrenal gland which, like the pituitary,
produces and releases into the blood a great many hormones of vital importance to the body. Without the hormones from the adrenals life would not be possible. One
condition resulting from undersecretion of the adrenal
glands is known as Addison's disease—named in honor of
the English doctor Thomas Addison who first recognized
and described the disease.

In Addison's disease there is an abnormal loss of water
and salt to the urine and an abnormal buildup of potassium in the body. Thus, the cells are bathed in an
abnormal intercellular sea. The patient suffers a gradual
loss of strength and energy and a wasting away of flesh,
as well as loss of appetite, severe vomiting, terrible pain
in the abdomen, extreme nervousness, and above all, low
blood pressure and kidney failure.

Normally the adrenal hormones regulate salt retention and potassium excretion by stimulating the nephron filters of the kidney. Since salt attracts and holds water, the adrenal hormones also indirectly assist the ADH of the pituitary in keeping water in the body. Thus, if the adrenal hormones are not secreted in adequate amounts, there is an abnormal loss of salt and water and a gain of potassium. The loss of water causes the low blood pressure, and this in turn causes inadequate filtration in the kidneys.

The adrenal glands may fail to produce and release sufficient hormones for a number of reasons, but the most common causes are tumors and tuberculosis of these glands. When so afflicted the glands are altered and injured to such an extent that they are unable to respond to the body's needs. Normally, the adrenals step up the output of their hormones when either the supply of salt is decreasing or the supply of potassium is increasing.

Let us now consider the tan mentioned earlier. Only recently has the tanning of the skin been explained. This may be because the tan has nothing to do with salt or water loss or potassium buildup but, rather, relates to a hormone of the pituitary gland called MSH.

The pituitary hormone MSH—melanocyte-stimulating hormone—stimulates the cells in the skin that produce melanin, a pigment which is responsible for the skin's natural color. The greater the amount of melanin the darker is the skin. The Negro has a large amount of melanin whereas the rare albino, who has perfectly white skin and pink eyes, has none. Normally, the adrenal glands regulate the amount of MSH present by inhibiting the pituitary's output of it. Thus, when the output of the adrenal hormones is reduced, the output of MSH is increased—causing the tanned skin of people with Addison's disease.

Before the availability of synthetic pituitary hormones, Addison's disease was considered fatal. Today, the disease can be treated with these hormones, often along with large dosages of common table salt, and the outlook for most victims of the disease is excellent.

chapter seventeen

KIDNEY FAILURE

The kidneys control all matters relating to the sea inside us. Should one kidney fail to function, the other usually keeps us going; should both fail, the results could be fatal. However, miracles can be performed—miracles of chemistry, miracles of physics, miracles of engineering, miracles of surgery—miracles having to do with the sea inside us.

The causes of kidney failure are numerous, the most common being infection, shock, injury, congenital abnormalities, poisoning, and transfusion reactions. Each of these can hamper a sufficient number of the kidneys' two million or so nephrons to cause serious trouble.

That injuries and infection can damage the nephrons is easily understood. In cases of congenital abnormalities, persons are born with destroyed or lazy nephrons. In shock the sharp and sudden drop in blood pressure has the effect of cutting off the blood supply to the kidneys.

What about poisoning? How does this cause kidney failure and shutdown? There are a number of poisons that cause particular damage to the nephrons—more damage, that is, than to other tissues and organs. Not only is the number of such poisons frightening, but many of them are often found about the house. Carbon tetrachloride, mercury, lead, copper, arsenic, phosphorus, boric acid, and DDT, for example, are all capable of causing death through nephron destruction and kidney failure.

Carbon tetrachloride is especially hazardous because it is cheap, widely used as a solvent, degreasing agent, "dry cleaner," or fire extinguisher and often is looked upon as being harmless. This chemical evaporates readily, and unless there is plenty of ventilation, it will quickly fill a room with lethal vapors. This is how most carbon tetrachloride poisonings occur. Boric acid, too, is cheap, widely used, and generally thought to be harmless. Harmless it is provided it does not get into the bloodstream. But if boric acid does get into the blood—which can happen accidentally if a dose of it is taken or it is put on an oozing, raw diaper rash—the result may be kidney shutdown.

What about a transfusion reaction? How does this cause kidney failure and shutdown? A transfusion reaction occurs when the patient's blood and the donor's blood are not compatible blood types and thus do not mix. Either the patient's or the donor's red blood cells disintegrate and in so doing release a pigment called hemoglobin—the pigment which makes red cells red. When so released hemoglobin is treated as a waste product and filtered out by the nephrons in the kidneys. But hemoglobin is not too soluble. When a large amount is present, as in this case, insoluble crystals form and plug up the nephrons, preventing normal waste materials from passing. The result is sudden kidney failure.

The kidneys, however, can withstand a great deal of injury before giving in. One authority estimates that two thirds of the nephrons in the two kidneys may be destroyed before the composition of the person's blood becomes excessively abnormal. This margin of safety is possible because the undamaged nephrons are able to come to the rescue by working overtime. But persons with such a condition are living with a greatly reduced margin of safety; the least increase in waste products—as the result of exercise, infection, eating too much, and so on—may easily present the overworked nephrons with more than they can handle.

Thus, the number of nephrons put out of commission is certainly a major deciding factor in the outcome of kidney failure. Of importance too is whether or not the nephrons are put out of commission permanently; if they are and a great number is involved, the result can be fatal. There is hope, however, even in severe cases, for doctors and scientists have learned a great deal about kidney function and are continuously developing more effective treatment.

Before we discuss treatment, let us consider what happens when the kidneys shut down: Wastes are not removed from the blood and thus they accumulate in and pollute the intercellular and cellular seas. The variety of wastes normally excreted by the kidneys is so numerous that, when they pile up inside the body, no specific substance can be considered the absolute cause of death. It could be urea, uric acid, creatinine, all three, or, more likely, the entire waste-product buildup as a whole.

There is, nonetheless, much evidence that a primary cause of death is the element potassium. Yet potassium is not a true waste—not a true waste, that is, in the sense that a certain amount of it is normal to the sea inside us and therefore essential to life. A certain number of cells are always disintegrating and thereby contributing their potassium to the intercellular sea—which contains less potassium than the cells. In illness, particularly kidney failure, the rate of cellular disintegration speeds up, causing a rise in potassium. Although we need potassium, an excess of it will stop the heart. This is often the cause of death in kidney shutdown.

In addition to too much potassium, there is also too much body water. Normally the kidneys excrete about a quart and a half per day; when the kidneys shut down often only an ounce or two is excreted, so that the bulk of the water taken in remains within the body to swell the tissues and cause edema. Or, water may escape into the lungs—just as in heart failure—and bring about death through drowning.

Further, the pH of the blood starts to drop because the kidneys are not removing acid wastes, which spells acidosis.

Thus there is too much potassium, too much water, and too much acid. What does the doctor do? What is the treatment?

First, the kidney victim must be rescued from drowning, so his water intake is restricted to the absolute minimum, that is, just enough to repay the water lost from the lungs and skin. Usually this amounts to somewhere around a quart a day. Because the patient is acutely ill this water allotment is invariably given by vein.

Further, the diet must be absolutely free of potassium. Protein foods, such as meat, fish, eggs, and cheese, which are rich in potassium, are actually deadly in kidney shut-down. But regardless of this dietary restriction the potassium content of the intercellular sea continues to go up, for the cells of the body continue to disintegrate and spill their potassium into the intercellular sea. Although there are chemical agents which when taken by mouth will couple up with potassium and remove it from the body, they have, for the most part, proved to be of limited use.

The answer, then, to severe kidney failure is an "artificial kidney," one which will remove potassium and acids and other wastes while the patient's kidneys are resting and recuperating. And herein lies a most interesting and wonderful fact: In most cases of kidney failure and kidney shutdown the kidneys do indeed spring back to complete health!

The principle of the artificial kidney can be demonstrated right on the kitchen table with five simple items— a piece of cellophane, starch, salt, Karo syrup, and a couple of drops of iodine. The cellophane is fashioned into a bag and half filled with a solution containing starch, salt, and Karo syrup. Karo syrup contains glucose, the very same sugar found in the blood. The bag is secured tightly at the neck by a string and immersed into a glass of plain water for about ten minutes. If the water is then tasted, sugar and salt can be detected, showing that both of these substances are made up of molecules small enough to pass through cellophane. Finally, a drop of iodine is added to the water. The water remains colorless which indicates that no starch is present, for starch and iodine produce an intense dark blue color. Thus, starch did not pass through the cellophane because of the large size of its molecules.

This simple experiment demonstrates a process known as dialysis. Dialysis is the separation of large and small molecules by means of a semipermeable membrane such as cellophane. Just as starch is separated from sugar and salt by dialysis, the small molecules can be separated from the large molecules in blood. And all the wastes in the blood are made up of small molecules. Therefore, if blood "is placed in a cellophane bag" and the "bag" immersed in water, potassium, urea, uric acid, and the like, pass, or diffuse, through the membrane and into the water.

The artificial kidney, then, operates on the principle of dialysis. In actual practice, of course, it is not quite as simple as putting blood in a cellophane bag. Moreover, there are several types of artificial kidneys, some small and cheap—one engineer made an artificial kidney from a kitchen kettle—and others large and expensive.

In the rotating-drum type of artificial kidney the patient's blood is run through several yards of cellophane tubing wound around a slowly rotating drum. The drum itself is immersed in a "bath" which contains glucose, salt, calcium, and a few other vital substances that are "small enough" to diffuse out of the cellophane tubing along with the waste products. (Blood cells, protein, and fat molecules are much too large to pass through cellophane.) Thus, for instance, the glucose which diffuses into the bath is balanced by the glucose which diffuses into the blood. But the troublemaker potassium is not balanced in this way since none is placed in the bath. The blood is cleansed, but not at the expense of its vital materials. The dialysis process is facilitated by the rotation of the drum.

In actual practice the patient is hooked up to the artificial kidney in the following way: One piece of plastic tubing (connected to the cellophane tubing) runs from an artery to the machine and another runs from the machine to a vein. Thus, the blood travels from the artery through

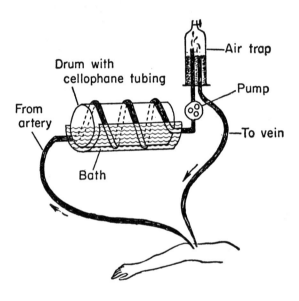

Artificial kidney

The artificial kidney in operation. In order to prevent the formation of blood clots—a very likely event when blood flows over a foreign surface such as cellophane—the patient is given an anticoagulant drug. The air trap permits the escape of any air bubbles which might form. (Air bubbles in the blood can prove fatal.) The victim of kidney failure is usually "hooked up" to the machine for an hour or two each day.

the cellophane tubing and into the vein. To assist the heart in moving the blood through the tubing, the machine is equipped with a small pump.

Blood, however, has a tendency to clot in the cellophane tubing and a blood clot could cause sudden death. To insure against this, the patient is given an anticoagulant, which is a drug that prevents clotting. Unfortunately, patients with bleeding tendencies cannot be given anticoagulant drugs. Too, air bubbles in the blood could also cause sudden death, and to prevent this from happening, the machine is equipped with an air trap or debubbler.

Again, most machines require specially trained doctors and technicians for efficient and safe operation. For these and other reasons a greatly simplified method has come into use—a method so simple that if need be it can be carried out right at home.

This new method is called peritoneal dialysis. Like the artificial kidney it operates on the principle of dialysis, but unlike the artificial kidney it uses the peritoneum instead of cellophane. The peritoneum is a delicate membrane which lines the walls of the abdominal cavity. Indeed, the peritoneum is so delicate that if the abdominal cavity is filled with water, wastes from the blood (there is a rich blood supply beneath the peritoneum) pass right through it into the water. Now, if instead of plain water a fluid of about the same chemical makeup as the bath of the artificial kidney is used, the result is a "natural artificial kidney."

In practice this is how it is done: The doctor makes a small incision below the navel and through the incision passes one end of a plastic tube into the abdominal cavity and connects the other to a couple of bottles containing the bath solution. The bottles are raised above the patient's bed and the solution allowed to run into the abdominal cavity. After the solution has been in the cavity an hour, the bottles are placed upon the floor. This causes the now polluted solution to run, via syphon action, back into the bottles. This is repeated twenty times or so, each time using two bottles of fresh solution. If necessary the entire series of "washings" may be repeated in two or three days.

Although peritoneal dialysis does not clean out the blood as thoroughly as the artificial kidney, and is therefore usually less desirable in advanced cases of kidney failure, it does serve as a life-saving substitute. In poisoning, for example, where dialysis works wonders by washing the poison right out of the blood, peritoneal dialysis compares favorably with the artificial kidney. Recently it saved the lives of four babies at a hospital nursery that had been given a formula mistakenly containing salt instead of sugar.

In summary, the artificial kidney and peritoneal dialysis afford a means of saving life in kidney failure. However, the failure or shutdown must be temporary, not permanent. The answer to permanent kidney damage is, for the present anyway, not at hand—except in the rare case where a kidney from a healthy person can be successfully substituted for a diseased kidney. This fascinating operation, called a kidney transplant, is best performed between identical twins, for identical twins are chemically alike and therefore will "accept" tissue from each other. Ordinarily, the body attacks and destroys transplanted foreign tissue with its antibodies. In several exciting instances, however, successful transplants have been made between two persons who were not twins—although usually of the same family—through the use of drugs which prevent the formation of antibodies.

The answer to permanent kidney failure will come, in all likelihood, in the form of an artificial organ, a miniature artificial kidney, which can be carried upon the body or even installed inside the body. One such device, about the size of a small matchbox, has been perfected already; others are sure to follow. Someday, perhaps soon, we may be able to pick one up at the corner drugstore.

chapter eighteen

THE BLOOD

Until now we have considered the blood, the body's red sea, purely as a fluid. Actually, blood consists not only of plasma (the watery fluid), but also red and white blood cells suspended in the plasma.

The blood of a healthy man averages, by volume, 50 percent plasma and 50 percent cells; the blood of a healthy woman averages 55 percent plasma and 45 percent cells. The proportion of plasma and cells in the blood of children varies. The newborn baby usually has more cells than plasma, whereas the teen-ager has more plasma than cells.

The percentage of cells is determined with a machine called a centrifuge. A sample of blood is placed in a test tube, and the tube is placed in the centrifuge where it spins at a high speed. Spinning—or centrifuging—causes the cells and the plasma to separate, so that when the test tube is removed from the machine there are two clearly defined layers. The almost colorless top layer is the plasma; the red bottom layer—the heavier layer—is the cellular portion. The percentage of cells in the blood, which is called the hematocrit, can be measured if the test tube has markings—or calibrations—on the side. If, for instance, a tube which has ten calibrations is filled with blood and the bottom cellular portion comes up to the fourth marking, the hematocrit is 40 percent; that is, the blood is 40 percent cells and 60 percent plasma.

The proportion of plasma and cells in the blood is of great value to the doctor in the diagnosis of disease. Suppose, for example, a sample of a man's blood is 20 percent cells and 80 percent plasma. His hematocrit is 20 percent, roughly 30 percent below the normal value of 50 percent for healthy men. The man has anemia—a severe deficiency of blood cells.

Or the hematocrit could be, for instance, 75 percent—a figure well above the normal 50 percent value. In this condition the proportion of plasma is so low that the red sea turns into "a stream of molasses" or thick blood; the blood does not circulate properly and is likely to clot—causing instant death. The "Red Sea" must be on the move; otherwise the cells are starved for oxygen and nutrients, and the wastes cannot be carried to the kidneys.

Thick blood usually stems from a loss of body water. In burns, for instance, the blood loses much of its plasma through damaged skin; too, severe sweating without drinking shoots up the hematocrit in a matter of minutes.

Or a high hematocrit may indicate cancer of the red cells, a disease called erythremia. In this disease a tremendous number of red cells pour into the blood from the bone marrow where they are made, and unless this is checked by the use of drugs, the outcome is fatal.

The plasma of the blood is a tributary of the body's great intercellular sea. It differs from other intercellular fluid, however, in that it contains a vastly greater number of dissolved substances, such as carbohydrates, proteins, fats, gases, minerals, hormones, enzymes, and antibodies. Like all things relating to the biological seas, there is balance over and above variety; that is, there is just so much salt, so much sodium bicarbonate, so much sugar, so much fat, so much protein, and so on.

A physical examination without a blood test (or analysis) is not too far from being worthless, for not uncommonly the blood can prophesize a disease weeks, months, or even years before it strikes. Often just one abnormal value alone will pinpoint a specific disease. Too much sugar almost always means diabetes; too much uric acid almost always means gout; too few antibodies means a lack of resistance to infection; and too much fat may mean hardening of the arteries. The list is almost endless. As one scientist put it ". . . . Blood is the mirror of health and disease."

There are numerous ways in which the body keeps the blood in a steady state. As we have seen, the kidneys carry the largest burden. Too, there are those unbelievable chemical messengers, the hormones, which often tell the kidneys what to do and when to do it.

Some hormones help keep the blood on an even keel without acting on the kidneys. Insulin, for example, keeps the blood sugar steady by allowing sugar to pass through the cell membranes into the cell. Another hormone of this type is parathormone. Though parathormone appears to have some action on the kidneys, this is not its chief role in the body.

Parathormone—or the parathyroid hormone—is manufactured by four very tiny glands called the parathyroids located on the back surface of the thyroid gland. The thyroid gland itself is situated in the front of the neck just below the voice box. Parathormone controls the amount of calcium dissolved in the plasma. When the amount, or concentration, of calcium starts to drop below the normal value, parathyroid glands increase their output of parathormone; when the concentration of calcium starts to rise, the glands decrease the output.

Once parathormone is released to the blood it is carried throughout the body. It is currently believed that the hormone acts primarily on bone cells, stimulating them to release to the blood a little of their stored calcium. Thus, through the ability of parathormone to flush out calcium from bone, normal calcium levels are maintained in the blood.

Too little calcium in the blood causes a frightening disorder called tetany. (Do not confuse tetany with tetanus. Tetanus is an entirely different ailment.) In tetany the muscles began to twitch, there are terrible belly cramps, and often violent convulsions.

This condition comes from a deficiency or lack of parathormone. That is, when the blood needs calcium parathormone is not there to flush it out of the bone. Sometimes there is a lack of the hormone because the parathyroid glands have become diseased. In years past, before scientists knew anything about the tiny parathyroids, they were often cut out unwittingly by the surgeon in the course of operating upon the thyroid. This may even happen accidentally in some instances today.

Too much parathormone often causes as much trouble as too little. If the parathyroid glands develop a tumor and grow beyond their normal size, excess parathormone can be produced, and thus excess calcium is washed out of the bones into the blood. When this happens, the kidneys attempt to remove this excess; but calcium is not too soluble in urine. Little crystals of calcium begin to form, and these grow and grow until they become stones —kidney stones! The presence of stones in the kidney can be compared to stones in the drainpipe of the kitchen sink. Unless the stones are removed, they will stop up the kidneys and the patient will die from the accumulation of toxic wastes.

But kidney stones are not all. The bones grow weaker and weaker because their very substance—calcium—is being washed away. They bend, they crack, they break. In the severe cases of long ago, before the doctors understood the disease, the entire skeleton gave way, turning the body into a human pretzel. The medical name for this weird deformity is almost as frightening as the disease itself—osteitis fibrosa cystica generalisata. Or, for the sake of brevity (but not much!) some call it Von Recklinghausen's disease—in honor of the German physician who was the first to recognize and describe the condition.

So much for calcium. Let us now turn to something else dissolved in blood plasma—the antibodies. Antibodies are chemical agents which protect the body against infection. They are manufactured by specialized cells, called plasma cells, which are located in the lymph nodes, tiny glandular structures scattered throughout the body. Further, plasma cells are not stimulated by the body, but by the germs that cause an infection!

Lockjaw, or tetanus, serves as an excellent example of

the action of antibodies. Lockjaw is a vicious disease caused by a germ which, under the microscope, looks like a tennis racket. Once this microbial monster gains entrance into the body it starts to multiply at a very rapid rate. The resulting millions and millions of germ cells release one of the most powerful poisons known to man.

The tetanus toxin (poison) is encountered by the plasma cells which start to produce a special type of antibody called antitoxin. Antitoxin unites chemically with the toxin and destroys its lethalness. A test tube of toxin—perhaps enough to wipe out the population of a good sized city—can be made perfectly harmless if an equal amount of antitoxin is added to it.

However, the plasma cells are taken unawares and may not be able to produce the antitoxin fast enough to quell the tetanus toxin. Thus the outcome can be fatal. On the other hand, if the victim survives the attack, the plasma cells continue making antitoxin long after the vicious invader has been defeated. If any of the deadly "tennis rackets" attack in the future there will be an abundance of antitoxins in the blood to take care of their deadly toxin. The body is now immune!

The body reacts similarly to other infectious diseases: The microbe, or its toxin, provokes the plasma cells to produce and release to the blood a special type of antibody. Eventually, the blood plasma will contain a galaxy of all kinds of antibodies—antibodies against tetanus, against whooping cough, against diphtheria, against polio, and so on.

The natural way to gain immunity, as we have seen, is to suffer the disease, but the plasma cells can be stimulated artificially to produce the antibodies for many diseases. In the process of vaccination a deactivated germ or its deactivated toxin is injected directly into the body. In the vaccination for lockjaw, for instance, a toxoid vaccine is used which is made by adding the chemical formaldehyde to the tetanus toxin. Although the toxoid is harmless, it stimulates the plasma cells to turn out antitoxin antibodies just as effectively as the deadly toxin.

Thus over the years the blood plasma accumulates, both naturally and artificially, a variety of antibodies. The very expression "childhood diseases," which is used for diphtheria, whooping cough, chickenpox, and the like, is testimony to the fact that with age comes immunity.

Interestingly, for the first few weeks of life, babies are generally as immune to infection as their parents. This is because the baby is born with a very large dose of antibodies obtained from its mother's blood—a dose large enough to protect it until the baby is able to manufacture its own antibodies. But the antibodies "inherited" from the mother soon break down and are excreted.

Occasionally, a person is born without the ability to manufacture antibodies, because something is wrong with the plasma cells. With this condition an infection which would normally be minor often proves to be fatal. Whereas the normal body continues to build up antibodies against various infections, those persons with faulty plasma cells are not as immune as on the day they were born.

This lack of antibodies is called agammaglobulinemia. When translated the name actually means the absence (*a-*) of antibodies (*-gamma globulin-*) in the blood (*-emia*). In severe cases of the disorder where the antibodies—or gamma globulins—are almost nonexistent, weekly, or monthly, doses of gamma globulin are life-saving. The gamma globulin the doctor injects is made from the plasma of normal human blood. Gamma globulin is terribly expensive, and in most instances treatment must be continued throughout life.

In addition to calcium, antibodies, and the other substances dissolved in the plasma (many of which were discussed in earlier chapters) there are the enzymes. Enzymes are the chemical keys of life, for without them all body functions would grind to a halt. Every single chemical reaction within the human body in order "to go" needs a specific enzyme—or chemical sparkplug—and unless the enzyme is there disease and even death may result.

Sometimes, people are born with an enzyme deficiency. For example, in a disease called galactosemia there is a lack of the enzyme needed to burn galactose, a sugar produced in the digestion of milk. Thus if the victim is given milk, galactose accumulates in the blood (which is what the word galactosemia means) and eventually poisons the brain, causing mental retardation. However, if the disease is diagnosed at birth, the baby can be given a milk substitute for three or four years, and mental retardation can be prevented.

Some diseases are accompanied by an increase in plasma enzymes. Such an increase could indicate certain forms of cancer, liver disease, kidney disease, or heart disease. Damaged cells release enzymes to the blood. Since each type of cell has a typical assortment of enzymes, the kind of enzyme that exists in excess often indicates the type of disease. In a heart attack, for example, the cells of the damaged area release an enzyme called LDH, and the LDH content of the blood rises. Not only does LDH signal a heart attack, but it also tells the doctor how the patient is coming along, for as the heart improves, the LDH content of the blood lowers to normal values. According to some heart specialists, the patient's "LDH profile" gives a better picture of the heart than the electrocardiogram.

The blood, then, is truly a mirror of what is going on in the human body, and with little doubt it is the doctor's best friend in the diagnosis of disease.

chapter nineteen

CLOTTING

Any mariner worthy of the name makes doubly sure that all the seams of a ship are properly caulked, for to keep the ship on the sea, the sea must be kept out of the ship.

The body too must be "caulked," for otherwise the sea inside us would eventually drain away and we would die. A tiny cut, or a bloody nose, could keep right on bleeding and bleeding and bleeding. But this is something most of us rarely think about because we know that blood is Nature's best caulker. Inside the body blood flows like water—and well it should as it is half water—but when it contacts the air blood clots and stops flowing.

Let us examine the principal chemical events involved in clotting, or coagulation, of the blood. The substances in the blood plasma involved in the clotting of blood include fibronogen, prothrombin, calcium, and other "factors," the identity or behavior of which are not fully understood. The most important, and most interesting, of the factors is Factor VIII—the antihemophilic factor.

In addition to fibrinogen, prothrombin, calcium, and Factor VIII, clotting also requires the presence of platelets. Platelets are specialized cells, much smaller than red and white blood cells, which are suspended in the blood plasma. The platelets begin the chain of events leading to the clot: At the site of the injury the platelets are attracted to the walls of the ruptured blood vessels. Here they become all jammed together and their cellular membrane disintegrates. When this happens, an enzyme called thromboplastin is released. But in order for the platelets to disintegrate and release thromboplastin, Factor VIII must be present. No Factor VIII, no thromboplastin—no clot!

Thromboplastin, in the presence of calcium, converts prothrombin into the enzyme thrombin; thrombin converts fibrinogen, a soluble protein, into an insoluble protein of long, sticky threads called fibrin. These threads intermesh through the blood, entrapping red and white blood cells and thereby forming a clot.

A person whose blood does not clot properly is called a bleeder. The most common and best known disease of this kind is hemophilia—a hereditary disorder wherein the victim has a deficiency of Factor VIII, the antihemophilic factor. Thus the platelets do not disintegrate and there is no chain of events leading to the clot.

The victim of hemophilia lacks Factor VIII because he has inherited a defective gene. Genes are unbelievably small particles present in the cell nuclei which carry the chemical blueprints for the processes of life. Each gene carries a particular set of instructions for a particular job, so if the gene is defective it is going to pass on the wrong information. In hemophilia, the defective gene does not carry the proper instructions for the manufacture of Factor VIII.

With rare exception, only the male suffers from hemophilia. However, the female transmits the disease to her children. There is a 50 percent chance that the sons of a carrier mother—a mother with a defective gene—will be hemophilic and her daughters carriers. The sons of a hemophilic father will carry no trace of the hereditary disease, unless his mother is also a carrier, because the defective gene is linked to the X chromosome—a chromosome which the male offspring never inherits from the father. (Chromosomes are colored bodies within the nucleus of the cell which carry the genes.) In stark contrast all the daughters of a hemophilic father will be carriers!

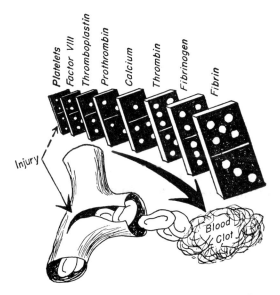

In the clotting, or coagulation, of blood one chemical sets off another in a chain reaction. If one chemical is lacking, or deficient, the clotting process is faulty; if one step in the chain is missing the others do not follow.

The outlook for the victim of hemophilia continues to be far from bright. Although transfusions with fresh blood and Factor VIII concentrates are often lifesaving, they are only temporary measures.

Another type of bleeder is a person with a deficiency of platelets—a disease called thrombocytopenia. Platelets are also called thrombocytes, and the medical term thrombocytopenia, when translated, means "a deficiency of thrombocytes in the blood." Thus, whereas the hemophiliac has platelets but lacks Factor VIII, the victim of thrombocytopenia has Factor VIII, but lacks platelets. Either way, little or no thromboplastin forms.

A deficiency of platelets may arise from a number of different causes. The bone marrow, which is where platelets are manufactured, may be lazy or poisoned; certain chemicals and drugs are harmful to bone marrow. Or there may be destructive forces, for certain germs will destroy platelets. An enlarged spleen will also cause platelet deficiency. Ordinarily, worn out platelets are destroyed in the spleen; when the spleen is enlarged too many platelets —the young as well as the old—are destroyed.

Bleeders with thrombocytopenia are usually in a better position than those with hemophilia because the cause can often be removed or corrected. Removal of an enlarged spleen, for instance, may bring dramatic results. Often, when drugs and chemicals are causing the trouble, they can be neutralized by the proper antidote.

A lack of vitamin K can also cause abnormal bleeding. Vitamin K is not directly involved in the clotting process, but it is one of the substances needed by the liver in the manufacture of prothrombin. Thus, when vitamin K is absent, prothrombin becomes deficient and blood fails to clot as it should.

Vitamin K is manufactured in the intestinal tract by beneficial bacteria that live there. These "bacteria . . . are always there," but if they are always there, how can a vitamin K deficiency be explained? Actually, there are three answers to this question. First, at birth there is not a single bacterium in the intestine. Second, something may happen to kill off the bacteria. Third, the vitamin K may not be absorbed from the intestine.

At birth bacteria do not exist in the intestine. They do not appear in sufficient numbers to produce vitamin K until after several hours of feeding. Thus, if bleeding should occur during the first few hours of life, the baby would not have enough prothrombin to clot its blood. Years ago the newborn bleeder was quite common, but today the doctor can prevent this situation by giving the mother a shot of vitamin K just before delivery. The vitamin passes from her blood through the placenta into the blood of the fetus via the umbilical cord. From the blood it enters the liver of the fetus and the manufacture of prothrombin begins.

Ordinarily, once bacteria establish themselves in the intestine, they remain there. However, big doses of penicillin and certain other antibiotics may kill them off, and then a deficiency of vitamin K may occur. This means a deficiency of prothrombin, and a deficiency of prothrombin means bleeding! But this situation can also be prevented, if the doctor gives vitamin K along with the antibiotic. Fortunately, when the antibiotic is stopped the bacteria return to the intestine.

Now for the third possibility, there may be a vitamin K deficiency because of faulty absorption. After vitamin K is produced by the bacteria, it dissolves in the fatty foods in the intestine and is absorbed along with these substances by the body. However, in order for dissolved fats to pass through the intestinal wall bile must be present. Thus, with a lack of bile there is a lack of vitamin K.

Gallstones are the most common cause of a lack of bile. By plugging up the bile ducts coming from the liver they prevent the bile from entering the intestine. Before the doctors knew about the relationship among vitamin K, bile, and prothrombin patients operated on for gallstones were in danger of bleeding to death. Today such patients are given dosages of vitamin K before the operation.

Another cause of excessive bleeding is a bad liver. Some persons are born with a bad liver; others acquire a bad liver because of infection, injury, or poisoning. The seriousness of the situation, depends of course, upon the degree to which the liver is damaged. The clotting abnormality may be slight, or in severe cases it may be as serious as hemophilia. A faulty liver leads to excessive bleeding because it fails to manufacture sufficient prothrombin and fibrinogen.

Not only man suffers from uncontrolled bleeding. About thirty years ago a farmer in Wisconsin was shocked to find that his cows were dying one after another in giving birth to calves. Although considerable bleeding is associated with the birth process, the loss of blood generally does not harm the mother. In this case, however, the cows were bleeders, and the open womb continued to bleed until there was no blood left for the heart to pump.

Within a matter of days scientists were scurrying about the man's farm trying to find the cause of the bleeding. The cattle had been fed sweet clover which had spoiled; Doctor K. P. Link and his fellow workers from the University of Wisconsin suspected that this spoilage had produced chemically a potent anticoagulant—that is, a chemical which prevents blood from clotting.

In 1940 Doctor Link's group isolated from the spoiled sweet clover a substance called Dicumarol—a chemical which has done much to revolutionize the treatment of diseases involving blood clots. Apparently, Dicumarol slows down the clotting process by "pushing aside" the molecules of vitamin K and thus interfering with the manufacture of prothrombin in the liver. A whopping dose of vitamin K will neutralize the effects of Dicumarol.

Dicumarol is clearly a vicious poison. A very close chemical relative, called warfarin, which is about forty times more potent than Dicumarol, is used as a rat poison. The rat bleeds to death! Yet, Dicumarol has proved to be of much value in the control of blood clots and associated disorders. And to think that this came about from "sweet clover disease."

Let us now consider the condition where blood clots when it should not. A clot within a blood vessel is a real threat to life, for if it should cut off the blood supply to a vital organ there may be instant death. The body is on guard against this possibility, however, and uses three very interesting means of defense.

One defense against the formation of clots within blood vessels has to do with electricity. The platelets possess a negative electrical charge. So, too, do the blood vessel walls. Since *like* electrical charges repel each other—*unlike* charges attract each other—the platelets normally do not stick to the vessel lining and therefore do not set off a clot. But injured vessels do, indeed, set off clots. Scientists now know that injured blood vessels lose their negative charge. Thus they no longer repel the platelets. In other words, by putting a negative charge on the vessel lining Nature prevents clotting; by removing the negative charge Nature prevents bleeding.

The other two defenses against wayward clotting involve two substances dissolved in the blood plasma—heparin and fibrinolysin. Heparin acts by sabotaging one or more steps in the clotting process. However, when blood vessels are injured—and the blood *should* clot—there are so many clotting factors released that heparin proves of no avail. And this, obviously, is the way it should be.

Fibrinolysin does not prevent clotting: rather, it dissolves little clots that have formed and are traveling in the bloodstream. Doctors and scientists now have good evidence that tiny clots are always turning up somewhere in the body. Nature is not perfect. Clots do form regardless of the body's negative charges, heparin, and fibrinolysin. Blood clots rank as the leading cause of sudden death.

The *overall* picture of what happens in most cases of "blood clot death" is now pretty well understood. As we get older our blood vessels start to collect fat just beneath the inside lining for reasons which are *not* understood. These fat deposits collect calcium and thereby grow harder and larger. In time these deposits break through the lining of the vessel—producing an *injury!* The negative charge is removed; the platelets start to collect and to disintegrate; and clotting commences. Once a clot is born, it may stay where it is and cause local trouble or it may break away and cause more serious trouble elsewhere.

Arteriosclerosis is the term used for hardening (sclerosis) of the arteries. Thrombosis is a condition where the patient has a blood clot (thrombus); in embolism he has a traveling blood clot (embolus). If a person has a blood clot or a thrombus, the clot may break away and become a traveling clot, or an embolus. Thus, arteriosclerosis leads to thrombosis, and thrombosis leads to embolism.

The coronary arteries—the arteries which supply blood to the heart muscle—are especially prone to arteriosclerosis. Thus coronary thrombosis—a clot in a coronary artery—is a common occurrence. Whether such a clot stays in the artery and grows larger and larger, or breaks away and enters a smaller branch, the particular area of the heart supplied by the blocked-off artery dies from a lack of blood.

Once a portion of the heart dies, the rhythm and the force of the organ as a whole is lost. There is terrible pain. This is the tragic event known as a heart attack. Whether or not the victim survives the attack depends on the size of the artery involved and how suddenly the artery was blocked off—and how strong the heart was in the first place. The sudden blocking of a major coronary artery is usually fatal for it will cause the sudden death of a great number of heart cells.

There is by no means unanimous agreement among the doctors as to the best treatment of heart attack. Some say long periods of absolute rest flat on your back; some say absolute rest sitting up in a chair; some say to get up and around as soon as you feel like it. Too, doctors do not agree as to whether anticoagulant drugs such as Dicumarol are of value. Although it would appear that these drugs help by preventing the clot from getting bigger, some reports fail to show much difference between patients who are given these drugs and those who are not.

Clots elsewhere in the body can also prove fatal. For instance, a clot that travels to the lung can cause sudden death. The doctor calls this a pulmonary embolism because it involves the lung (pulmonary) and a traveling clot (embolism). But death from this cause has been reduced through the use of Dicumarol and similar drugs; the best results are obtained with an anticoagulant called Coumadin—which is really warfarin, the rat poison mentioned earlier! Thus, although a chemical acts as a poison at one dose, it may act as a drug at a lower dose.

In summary, then, our internal red sea has a built-in caulking system which is set into operation when blood vessels are damaged.

chapter twenty

TRANSFUSIONS

Although the idea of replacing lost blood must truly be ancient, it is only within the past fifty years or so that the practice has emerged as the doctor's chief life line in emergency situations. Even under the best circumstances giving one man's blood to another is a serious business. Any foreign substance injected into the body can be dangerous, and in the case of blood it can easily prove deadly. Thus, when the physician and surgeon of long long ago tried to give blood transfusions, they had poor results and soon gave it up. Some patients survived when given blood, but most were not so fortunate.

One of the first advances in the field came with the realization that death after a transfusion results from a reaction between bloods that do not mix. Some bloods mix and others do not, but what is meant by "mix"?

This can be illustrated by a laboratory demonstration: A sample of type A blood is poured into a centrifuge tube and a pinch of anticoagulant is added to prevent the blood from clotting. The tube is spun at a high speed in the centrifuge to separate the plasma and the cells. Next a sample of type B blood is centrifuged to separate the plasma and cells.

After the plasma and cells of each of the blood samples are separated, a drop of type A plasma is added to a drop of type B cells, and a drop of type B plasma is added to a drop of type A cells. This is done on a piece of glass with a white background. The two mixtures are stirred well with a toothpick. In less than a minute a peculiar and startling effect occurs: "Giant" red clumps are formed. The red cells have all joined together—that is, they have agglutinated.

Something in the plasma of type A blood causes the cells of type B blood to agglutinate, and something in the plasma of type B blood causes the cells of type A blood to agglutinate. These "somethings" are special antibodies called agglutinins. Type A blood plasma contains anti-B agglutinins, and type B blood contains anti-A agglutinins. The anti-A agglutinins of type B blood plasma react with a factor called A in the red cells of type A blood and thus agglutinate the blood. The anti-B agglutinins of type A blood plasma agglutinate type B blood cells by reacting with a factor in the red cells called B.

Thus, blood types are named after the factors present in the red cells. Type A blood is named A for the factor A in its red cells—although its plasma contains anti-B agglutinins. Type B blood is called type B for the factor B in its red cells. (Its plasma contains anti-A agglutinins.) Type A blood and type B blood do not mix because the agglutinins of one agglutinate the cells of the other, and thus, the two bloods destroy each other.

In addition to type A and type B, there are two other

blood types—type AB and type O. The red cells of type AB blood contain both factor A and factor B. The red cells of type O blood do not contain either factor A or factor B. Further, type AB blood plasma contains no agglutinins, whereas type O blood plasma contains both anti-A agglutinins and anti-B agglutinins.

To tell whether a person is type A, B, AB, or O requires but a couple of minutes. A tiny prick is made in the finger and a drop of blood placed on each end of a glass slide. To one drop is added a drop of type A plasma (which contains anti-B agglutinin) and to the other drop a drop of type B plasma (which contains anti-A agglutinins) is added. If both drops of blood agglutinate, factor A and factor B are both present in the red cells and the blood type is AB; if neither drop agglutinates, neither factor A nor factor B is present in the red cells, and the type is O; if the drop treated with B plasma ("anti-A") agglutinates, factor A is present and the type is A; and if the drop treated with A plasma ("anti-B") agglutinates, factor B is present and the type is B.

In addition to the "A–B system," there are other factors in the blood. Of these, the most important is the Rh factor. (The symbol Rh stems from experiments which were performed using rhesus monkeys.) Blood is either Rh positive (Rh$^+$) or Rh negative (Rh$^-$). If the red cells contain the Rh factor, the blood is Rh positive, and if this factor is missing, the blood is Rh negative. About 85 percent of the population is Rh positive and 15 percent Rh negative. The rarest blood type of the A–B system is type AB, and thus the rarest blood of all is AB, Rh negative.

If a person who is Rh negative receives Rh positive

A plasma   B plasma

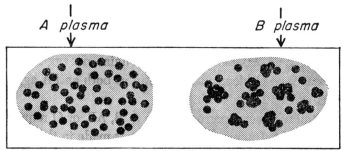

TYPE A

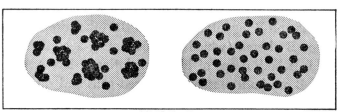

TYPE B

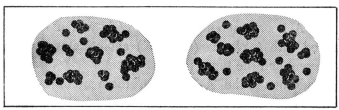

TYPE AB

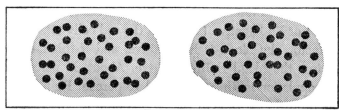

TYPE O

blood, the Rh factor in the red cells of the Rh-positive donor blood stimulates the plasma cells of the recipient's immunity system to make agglutinin antibodies in the same way that microbes stimulate the production of other antibodies. For the first transfusion there is usually no trouble, but if ever this person were to receive Rh positive blood again the agglutinin concentration would shoot up so high that mass agglutination of the donor's blood would occur within the vessels.

About one out of every fifty children born to Rh negative mothers and Rh positive fathers has a blood disorder called erythroblastosis fetalis—which means "a destructive type of anemia in the fetus, or unborn child." What happens is as follows: The fetus inherits the Rh factor from the father and is therefore Rh positive. Since red cells are constantly disintegrating (and this is normal), some of the Rh factor is released and enters the mother's circulation via the placenta. As a result the mother's plasma cells are stimulated to produce antibodies; these eventually make their way into the fetal blood and there agglutinate and destroy red cells. Often the destruction is so severe

---

To find a person's blood type, illustrated on facing page, a drop of his blood is placed on each end of a glass slide. Then to one drop is added a drop of type A blood plasma (which contains anti-B agglutinins) and to the other drop a drop of type B blood plasma (which contains anti-A agglutinins). If agglutination occurs in both drops, the person's red cells contain both factor A and factor B (type AB); if neither agglutinates, the red cells contain neither factor A nor factor B (type O). Type A blood is agglutinated only by type B blood plasma; type B blood is agglutinated only by type A blood plasma.

that the baby is stillborn. This is especially likely to happen with the third and fourth child, because each pregnancy brings about a greater outpouring of antibodies. The first child often either escapes the disease or has a very mild case.

The treatment of erythroblastosis fetalis involves a complete blood exchange. The infant is given a transfusion of Rh-negative blood, and at the same time, bled to remove the polluted blood. When an Rh positive man marries an Rh negative woman, the only way they can prevent this frightful disease is to limit the size of their family. However, a group of doctors recently reported encouraging results with a serum that prevents the Rh factor from stimulating the mother's plasma cells. Perhaps this will be the answer.

When a person is given blood of the wrong type a transfusion reaction occurs and death may result. Precisely what happens? First, there is, as we have already seen, agglutination or the clumping together of the red cells. Although this sounds a lot like blood-clot trouble and thrombosis, these clumps behave somewhat differently. Instead of growing and growing and getting bigger and bigger, like a true clot, they disintegrate and release hemoglobin—the coloring matter of the red cells—to the plasma. When the blood circulates through the kidney the hemoglobin is treated as a waste and filtered out into the urine. Hemoglobin is not too soluble, and thus it forms insoluble crystals in the kidney nephrons. This plugs up the nephrons and the upshot is kidney failure.

In addition to factor A, factor B, and the Rh factor, red cells may contain other factors which may cause transfusion reactions, such as factors Hr, M, N, and P. Therefore, even though the donor's blood and the recipient's blood are of the same type so far as the A, B, and Rh factors are concerned, safety demands that they be "cross matched" before blood is given.

In the cross-match test, each of the two bloods is centrifuged. Then a small quantity of donor red cells is mixed with a small quantity of recipient plasma and a small quantity of recipient red cells is mixed with a small quantity of donor plasma. If none of the cells are agglutinated, it can be assumed that the two bloods match each other. On the other hand, if agglutination or clumping occurs the bloods are mismatched. For instance, even though donor X and recipient Y have, let us say, type A, Rh positive blood, cross matching may show that they are mismatched. If they are mismatched, the donor blood is ordinarily not suitable.

In the early days of blood transfusion, a rubber tube, equipped with needles at both ends, was run from an artery of the donor to a vein of the recipient. Blood was then allowed to flow until the donor fainted or the recipient showed signs of improvement. Today, transfusions are usually made through the blood bank. Blood is collected from the donor in sterile pint bottles containing a small amount of sodium citrate and glucose. The citrate prevents the blood from clotting and the glucose serves as a source of nourishment for the blood cells during storage. The blood so collected can be used immediately or it can be stored for a period of up to three weeks at a temperature of 39°F.

In situations where blood is not available, where adequate quantities of different blood types cannot be stocked, or where there is no time for cross matching, such as on the battlefield, blood substitutes are used. These substitutes do not supply vital red cells—which carry the oxygen to the tissues. But they do repay lost fluid, which prevents a drop in blood pressure and thus shock. Shock is the usual cause of death in hemorrhage. Blood substitutes can be given without regard to blood type because they do not contain red cells.

The most commonly used blood substitutes are plasma, saline, and dextran. Plasma is the next best thing to whole blood because it supplies everything except the cells. It is made by centrifuging whole blood and then pouring off the plasma portion into an evaporator. In the evaporator water is driven off and the plasma reduced to a powder which is then placed in sterile pint bottles. In this form it may be stored indefinitely. Just before it is used sterile distilled water is added.

Saline may also be used as a blood substitute, if necessary. Though the bulk of it seeps out of the capillaries soon after it is given, enough remains within to keep the circulation going for a while. With a mild to moderate loss of blood, saline may do the job alone. With a severe loss of blood, it may keep the patient alive until blood becomes available. Saline is a solution of 0.9 percent salt in water. It is made to contain exactly 0.9 percent salt because this concentration is isotonic; that is, it has the same osmotic density as the red cells. Thus, when the cells receive saline they neither shrink nor burst. Giving a large amount of plain water by vein would cause death because the red cells would burst and release their hemoglobin.

Perhaps no one will ever discover the perfect blood substitute, but the substance dextran comes astonishingly close to it. Dextran is a white powder made from sugar beets; chemically it is related to corn starch. In transfusions a solution of 6 percent dextran in saline is used. Unlike plain saline, dextran does not ooze out of the capillaries. And rarely are there any serious side effects with dextran.

In addition to blood and blood substitutes, there is a variety of other life-saving solutions—solutions which are often just as vital. These include sugar solutions, such as glucose, to supply calories and water; mineral solutions to supply salt, potassium, and calcium; amino acid solutions to supply protein; and solutions to supply key vitamins. What is more, these basic solutions are available to the doctor in endless combinations. Thus, the doctor can put his hand on just the right bottle to suit individual requirements, and an individual who would not have lived years ago can now be saved. The "magic" of these solutions has arisen from the work of the scientists and doctors who have devoted their lives to the sea inside us.

INDEX